FOOD HYGIENE
AND FOOD HAZARDS

Food Hygiene
and Food Hazards

for all who handle food

A. B. CHRISTIE,

MA, MD, FRCP, FFCM, DPH, DCH,

Honorary Physician, Fazakerley Hospital, Liverpool
lately Head of Department of Infectious Diseases,
University of Liverpool
Professor of Infectious Diseases, University of Benghazi, Libya

and

MARY C. CHRISTIE

National Diploma, Hotel and Catering Institute

FABER AND FABER
3 Queen Square
London

First published in 1971
by Faber and Faber Limited
3 Queen Square, London WC1

Reprinted 1972
This Second edition first published in this format 1977

Printed in Great Britain by
Whitstable Litho Ltd., Whitstable

All rights reserved

ISBN 0 571 10902 0 (paper covers)
ISBN 0 571 04949 4 (hard-bound edition)

Contents

7

CONTENTS

PART 3

List of Illustrations

Figures

9

Preface to the second edition

In preparing the second edition of this book we have, of course, had to re-read the first. We have been glad to find very little with which we disagreed, and indeed we have been deeply touched by the many kind comments made about our book in letters both from home and abroad. We cannot claim that our first edition has led to a decrease in food poisoning, or to a perceptible rise in the standards of food hygiene. Indeed we have had to include in this second edition details of two food-poisoning organisms not mentioned in the first, *Bacillus cereus* and *Vibrio parahaemolyticus*. But we have been encouraged by the adoption of our book as a textbook in several catering colleges and schools, and we have been surprised at the number of housewives who seem to have read the book. We have accordingly added a chapter on the role of the housewife as customer and food hygienist, a role which is of great and final importance. Housewives are not all stay-at-homes these days, but travel far and wide with their husbands and families, and we have added a chapter on the possible food hazards of twentieth-century travel. Holidays can be marred by faults in food hygiene and we have included an account of an unusual outbreak in a holiday camp.

We are indebted to our publishers for patience and forbearance while we prepared this edition separated by a few thousand miles.

A. B. CHRISTIE
MARY C. CHRISTIE

Liverpool and Tripoli, 1976

Preface to the first edition

Food is a homely word, poisoning an outlandish one. Thrown together, they make a startling sound, food poisoning. This is surely an extraordinary combination, food which nourishes us and poison which destroys us. Yet food poisoning is not exotic, but a hazard of everyday life. Very few of us have not suffered an attack, though often mild and unrecognized. When an explosive outbreak occurs, there is no doubt about the diagnosis.

Food poisoning should never occur. Enough is known about food-poisoning germs, their habits of life and method of spread. We ought to be able to destroy or control them. The reason we fail is that not enough people have this knowledge. Very often the people who ought to know are ignorant—the producers and distributors of food, the manufacturers of food products, the shopkeeper who sells and the chef who cooks the food: in short, the food handler.

We have tried in this book to present the facts. Many of these facts are unpleasant, but we have not hesitated to state them. At the same time, we believe that our theme is an absorbing one, and that, behind some of the horrors, there is a gripping tale of bacterial warfare. Parts of the tale are really detective stories.

The senior author has spent a lifetime studying infection, grappling with its final results at the bedside of his patients, but also following the trail of infection far outside his hospital walls. The junior author, his daughter, is more at home in a hotel than a hospital, and is still near enough her student days in Hotel School not to have forgotten the student's outlook. Together they have tried to write a book that will appeal to a wide range of readers.

We would like to feel that our book will be useful to students of

11

the hotel and catering industry and to all who have to face examinations in food hygiene. Ideally, we would like all who have to handle food to look through our pages. Catering officers in hospitals, institutions and canteens, as well as managers and chefs in hotels, ought to know the facts of food hygiene. Public Health Inspectors deal every day with food hygiene problems: our book we hope will help them in their difficult job, and also be helpful to those in training. Hospital sisters and nurses should know in detail the mechanism of infection that brings patients with food poisoning under their care, and the danger of outbreaks occurring even in ward and hospital kitchens.

We would, of course, hope for an even wider audience, not in order to make our fortune from royalties, but because the facts of food hygiene concern everyone, though they are known only to the few. Our book might therefore find its way into teachers' training colleges, so that those who have a chance to teach can pass on the facts. It might not be out of place as a general science book for upper school forms, for although we have tried to write in the simplest of styles, the book is based on accurate biological facts. Schoolgirls studying for G.C.E. examinations in domestic science should find it useful and the housewife who has left her schooldays behind her might read it with profit, both as regards her own kitchen and her shopping. Whoever reads it we hope will profit from it. Above all, if readers are in a position to do so, we hope they will apply its lessons where it is needed—in the production, distribution, preparation and serving of the food we eat.

A. B. CHRISTIE
MARY C. CHRISTIE

Liverpool, 1970

Part 1

1

The Fight for Food

Man the hunter

All animals hunt, eat and sleep. Primitive man did just that—he caught his food, ate it, and slept it off. He added a few roots and berries and perhaps some leaves and nuts to his diet of flesh, and maybe he learned to store some of these against a hungry period; but most days he was up and out and after his prey, and the quest for food was, as for all other animals, his one and only occupation. It is not known whether he ever suffered from food poisoning. If he did, the outbreak was limited to the occupants of his cave, for the cave-dweller hunted only for his own, and did not set up as a wholesaler or distributor of his kill. On the walls of his cave he drew the animals he hunted, and he may have hoped thereby to influence the luck of the chase; if so, it was his only attempt to manipulate his food supply, for this was otherwise a ruthless affair of hunting, killing and eating. There was neither time nor opportunity for sophistication.

Business man

Modern man has no time to hunt. He is too busy checking invoices, cabling foreign brokers, or feeding his computers. Ships sail into his ports and, if there is no strike on, vast cargoes are unloaded into warehouses, and giant lorries pound their way thence down motorways to inland markets. At home he has long since regimented his animals and, instead of hunting them, he confines them within fences or buildings. He cares for them indeed, exhibits them at shows and festoons them with medallions. At the same time he grossly exploits their natural functions, especially those of procreation and milk production. When their time comes, he does not fell them where they graze, but ships them in trucks to markets where they are herded with truck-loads of other animals, also on their last pilgrimage. Finally they reach the abattoir lairs, and finish up as so much dead meat on the slaughter-house floor. It is a highly complicated business, and much more ruthless than the primitive hunt.

Commercial man

Modern man has also organized the products of the earth. He no longer accepts nature as he finds her, but rips and tears the land with steel, strews it with chemicals, and allows only those plants to grow which measure up to his demands. When the crops are ripe, they are not eaten by the man who grew them, but go off in lorry-loads to mills, markets, warehouses, distributors, food factories and retailers. It may be months or years before the final product reaches the table, where it may form an unrecognizable ingredient of some *plat du jour*, and be eaten by a diner so civilized that he has forgotten that the delicacy before him comes from the field and the chase. All this is, of course, modern commerce, and without it modern life could not go on, but it brings problems. The caveman might occasionally come to grief from eating a poisonous berry, or a chunk of killed carcass left too long in his cave: but modern man puts a vast amount of manipulation and sophistication into the production of his food, and in the process runs far greater risks than his less demanding cave-man ancestor.

Man the animal

Man is an animal. No matter how modern he may be, or how highly civilized may be the life he leads, he still needs food suitable for an animal. Unfortunately many other animals like the same kind of food. Rats flourish if they can get their teeth into food intended for humans, and a mouse will risk its life for a piece of cheese. Dogs and cats often share their owner's food, though cats can be fussier than their owners about what they will or will not eat; yet a tin of cat food differs very little, as far as proteins, fat or carbohydrates are concerned, from a tin of meat for humans. The main difference is in the label.

Germs share his food

The greatest menace to man's food supply comes, however, not from cats, dogs, rats, mice and other visible animals, but from the hordes of invisible living organisms that also like the food man eats. These organisms are usually called micro-organisms, because they can be seen only under a microscope, but it is simpler to call them just germs. A germ consists of one cell only—it is unicellular. Man's body consists of countless numbers of cells—he is a multicellular animal. Yet a unicellular germ can cause disease or even death in multicellular man, if it can attack him under favourable conditions. Access to man's food supply provides such favourable conditions and all the complications of modern food production make such access all too easy. Some germs flourish and multiply enormously in food, and when an unsuspecting person eats some of it, he may go down with food poisoning, or even something worse like typhoid fever.

The germs that invade our food belong to many different families or races, and, just like humans, they have different habits and modes of life. Some germs called staphylococci find a cream bun or custard trifle much to their liking, provided it is neither too hot nor too cold. Others such as *Clostridium welchii* revel in a lukewarm stew. Salmonellae like meat, especially cold meat; if they can get inside a nice meat pie after it is cooked and cold, they begin to enjoy life, and multiply rapidly, but they hate heat. If the pie is well heated before it is eaten, the salmonellae are all killed and cause no harm, whereas if the pie is eaten cold, the unfortunate person who eats it may get salmonella food poisoning. Some germs produce poisonous substances called toxins while they are multiplying in food, and these toxins may be heat-resistant. When such food is heated the germs may be killed, but the toxins may not be destroyed, and the food, though it contains no live germs, may still cause food poisoning.

Clearly, before we can attack all these germs, we must know

quite a lot about them. The general of an army spends a great deal of time studying his enemy; he tries to forecast how his enemy will behave, and then he plans his own manoeuvres to try to upset his enemy's. In the same way, to prevent food poisoning we must study food-poisoning germs, trying to understand exactly how they get into our food, and how they behave when they are in. Only then can we adapt our methods of food production and preparation to prevent these germs from spoiling our food. This is what is involved in food hygiene, and this is what this book is about.

2

A Day in the Life of a Germ

The main difference between a man and a germ is size. The man is much bigger. Their lives are otherwise similar: they eat, grow, reproduce and die. Man spends a great part of his life sleeping, but most germs have no time for this—their life is too short. It takes a man 40 years to grow, reproduce, and bring his offspring to maturity, but a germ can do all this in 20 minutes. By the end of 24 hours, one germ can produce many thousands of millions of offspring. It can do this only if everything is in its favour. If conditions are against it, a germ may die in a few seconds. What, for germs, are the facts of life?

Food and growth

If one were to look inside a bacteriology laboratory or, even worse, a textbook of bacteriology, one would be impressed by the great difficulty scientists have in coaxing germs to grow. Special media have to be prepared. These usually consist of jelly or broth to which specially chosen carbohydrates, proteins, vitamins or other chemicals have to be added; sometimes human or animal blood has to be added as well. The acidity of the medium has to be carefully adjusted. A piece of the substance thought to be contaminated is mixed with sterile water or saline and a drop of this is added to the medium. The bottle of broth or plate of jelly is placed in an incubator which must be kept at a set temperature; if this is only a degree or two wrong, the germ may not grow. Even the amount of oxygen must be regulated; some germs require a lot, some cannot stand more than a trace.

Some germs will not respond to all this care. They grow only on living cells, and the bacteriologist must get such cells from animal or human tissues and keep them alive in the laboratory so that he can try to grow these germs on them. These are known as tissue cultures and are used mainly for growing viruses. Viruses are very small germs which grow only in living cells. However, some germs will not grow even in tissue cultures, but only if injected into live animals. This is why animals such as rats, mice and guinea-pigs have to be used in laboratories.

Laboratory life

All this seems very complicated. Surely germs are all over the place and do not appear to have much difficulty in surviving outside the laboratory. They can thrive on the skin of one's nose, on the wing of a dead bird or in the dry dust on a window ledge. This, of course, is true and it is the artificiality of the conditions in the laboratory that makes things so difficult. It is very much the same with human beings. In the artificial conditions which have to be set up round a diseased or injured patient, keeping the patient alive can be an extremely difficult affair. He may need a machine to keep his breathing going, the amount of oxygen he needs must be calculated, and measures must be taken to regulate his temperature. If he cannot take food by mouth, nourishment must be given directly into a vein, and this can raise great problems. It is easy to give a carbohydrate such as glucose intravenously, but very difficult to give even the simplest proteins or fat. The amount of fluid that goes into and comes out of the patient's body must be measured. A highly skilled team of doctors and nurses is required. A visitor from outer space seeing this for the first time might conclude that human beings led a most precarious existence. He would not realize that the same human being, when well, gives not a thought to how he breathes or how his temperature is maintained, drinks as much as he likes, and eats anything that takes his fancy from rhubarb to sharks' fins or birds' nests. Neither man nor germs show up well under artificial conditions.

Where germs live

Under natural conditions germs flourish almost anywhere.

Fig. 1. Germs flourish almost anywhere: the arrows point
to some of the places

Some food-poisoning germs can live in garden soil for as long as a
year. They have also been found growing in waste-pipes from
wash-basins and water-closets, and in dry floor dust. They can
live in water for weeks on end, but they can also survive in a dry
crack in a table top; but they are happiest living on some other
animal as parasites. Staphylococci, for example, live very well on
human skin. They may be found in the fold of a nail, on the edge
of an eyelid, deep in the armpit or anywhere else on the body.
Normally they do us no harm, but they can cause a whitlow on the
finger, a stye on the eye, an abscess in the armpit or some much
more serious condition. From our skin they easily get on to
towels, dish cloths, rolling-pins and table napkins. If they get into
our food, they can cause food poisoning.

Salmonellae live in the intestinal tract of many animals: the list includes rats, pythons, tortoises, pigeons, cattle and pigs as well as man. They get into the host—the technical name for the infected animal—by first multiplying in its food supply and then being swallowed. All kinds of food can be invaded by food-poisoning germs, though different germs prefer different foodstuffs. This will be considered in more detail in later chapters. However, germs cannot jump on to food. They must be placed on it or carried to it, and so it is usually food that is handled a lot that becomes contaminated with germs. Pies, cold meats, salads, trifles and creams are obvious examples. These are all foods that may be prepared a long time before being eaten. This is another important point; one or two germs on food can easily be eaten without harm, but if the germs have had time to multiply in the food, the one or two become many millions and an outbreak of food poisoning results.

Geography of germs

Germs are found all over the world, and nowadays they do not stay put, for modern methods of food production and distribution give them every chance to roam. Germs have, in fact, become great travellers, and round-the-world trips are commonplace with them. Heidelberg is a pleasant German university town, but it is also the name of a food-poisoning germ which was first described there in 1933, but has since become common all over Europe and in America. Johannesburg, Montevideo, Tennessee and Singapore, among nearly a thousand other places, have also given their names to germs that have since wandered far from home. This ability of germs to survive long periods of travel is one of the characteristics of food-poisoning germs to which we shall have to refer frequently in later chapters.

How germs survive

Germs have a fairly tenacious hold on life. They can put up with all sorts of discomfort. Most of them can survive drying. Dysentery germs, for example, can live for weeks on bits of blotting-paper, on cotton-wool balls, on bits of dry sticks and on metal tags. They have survived for over a fortnight on the wooden seat of a water-closet, a fact which raises an obviously important point of personal hygiene. This resistance to drying is true of many of the food-poisoning germs, so that if they once get into a kitchen, a bakehouse, or any place where food is handled, they can persist in the dust on tables, floors and ledges, and be a source of danger for quite some time.

Effect of cold

Germs can stand almost any degree of cold. It is in fact customary to preserve germs in laboratories, especially viruses, by storing them at −70° C. Freezing-point is 0° C., so that −70° C. is cold indeed, but some germs can stand such temperatures for months or years on end. Germs can therefore easily survive in frozen food. They cannot multiply at such temperatures. In fact, they stop multiplying at temperatures well above freezing-point. That is why we keep food in refrigerators to prevent germs from multiplying. If there are one or two germs on the food when it is put into the refrigerator at night, there will still be only one or two on it in the morning. If the same food had been left in a warm room, there might have been countless millions of germs in the food by daybreak.

Effect of heat

Germs like a little warmth, but most of them cannot stand heat, and are very easily destroyed by it. Most salmonellae, for example, are killed in 15 to 20 minutes at 60° C. (140° F.); this is 40° below boiling-point and is not really very hot. Most cooking methods heat the food well above 60° C. This is lucky for us, though unlucky for salmonellae. Some food-poisoning germs are not so easily destroyed by heat. *Clostridium welchii* spores survive boiling for several hours, so that if the germ gets into food and multiplies in it, cooking may not destroy it. Staphylococci are easily killed by cooking, but if they have already produced toxin in the food, the toxin may resist the heat of cooking though the germ itself dies.

23

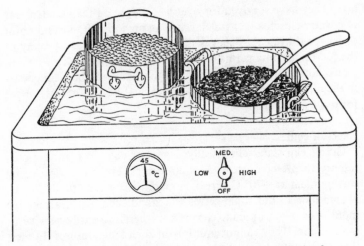

FIG. 2. Germs like a little heat, e.g. the gentle warmth of a
bain-marie water-bath as used in catering establishments

Spores

Some germs exist in two different forms—the vegetative and the
spore form. These can best be explained by thinking of the life-
cycles of some animals. A squirrel is full of life in the summer, but
in the winter it hibernates, or goes into a state where all its living
processes are slowed down; it can sleep in this state for weeks on
end without waking for food. The spore of a germ can be likened
to the hibernating state of the squirrel, the vegetative form to its
active summer life. In the sporing state, a germ can survive for
many years. Spores can often resist very high temperatures. The
vegetative form of the germ which causes botulism, *Clostridium
botulinum*, is killed by heating for 10 to 15 minutes at 80° C.
(176° F.), but its spore can resist boiling for hours. This is obviously important if a spore gets into food, but not all germs form
spores. A germ in the vegetative state is full of life and multiplies
quickly. In this state it is usually easy to kill by heat and other
means.

24

In this chapter we have seen in general terms how germs live and die. In the next chapter we shall consider the life histories of food-poisoning germs in more detail before we go on to study how they get into food, and how we must try to prevent this.

3

Food-poisoning Germs

Almost any germ can cause a gastro-intestinal upset if it gets into food and multiplies quickly in it. Even germs which are normally harmless can do this, but only when the food is prepared under very bad conditions with no thought for food hygiene. The germ which is present in everyone's intestinal tract, *Escherichia coli*, is one of those. It normally causes no harm so long as it stays in the bowel; in fact it probably carries out important functions in the bowel; but it sometimes causes trouble when it gets into food. There are, however, germs which have a special liking for human food; they multiply very readily in it, and cause typical symptoms in people who eat the contaminated food. These include the salmonellae, some clostridia, shigellae and staphylococci. We must consider them in some detail, but first a few words about their names.

The naming of germs

Germs get their names in many different ways. *Escherichia coli*, for example, is called after the bacteriologist Escherich who first described it in 1885. Colon is the Greek word for bowel, so that *Escherichia coli* is simply a bowel germ called after its discoverer. Mercifully it is usually called just *E. coli*. Salmonellae are called after Dr. Salmon, and shigellae after Dr. Shiga. Shigellae are the germs which cause dysentery. Dysentery itself comes from another Greek word, *enteron* meaning bowel, and the *dys* signifies something wrong. One very well-known dysentery germ is *Shigella sonnei*, and Dr. Sonne was a Danish doctor who described it. Staphylococci comes from two Greek words, *staphylee*, which means a bunch of grapes, and *coccus* which means berry, and the germs under the microscope do look like a bunch of grapes or berries. *Clostridium welchii* is a germ called after Dr. Welch, but in *Clostridium botulinum* the second word comes from the Latin, *botulus*, meaning sausage. The term was first used after an outbreak of botulism in Germany in 1793 which caused severe illness in 13 people who shared a large sausage. Clostridium comes from a Greek word, *closteer*, meaning a thread or spindle, and refers to the shape of the germ when swollen by its spore. Brucellae are the cause of brucellosis, a milk-borne disease, and the germ is named after Dr. Bruce who found this germ in the spleen of four patients who died of the disease in Malta in 1887.

Families of germs

Germs, like human beings, belong to families; they have a family name and an individual name. The family name always comes first and the individual name second. *Salmonella dublin* is the full name of a germ in the salmonella family; its individual name dublin comes from the town Dublin where it was first described. The family name always has a capital when the full name is used, and the second name a small letter, even when it is the name of a person or town; and the full name is always printed in italics. Other places which have given their names to salmonellae are Aberdeen, Brandenburg, Chicago, Georgia, Kentucky, London, Newport and Singapore, and there are very many more. Some salmonellae are named after their discoverer, e.g. *Salmonella thompson* and *Salmonella virchow*; some after the animals they infect, e.g. *Salmonella pullorum* and *Salmonella gallinarum*, both parasites of poultry—the second names are both Latin for hens. Some are called after the diseases they cause, e.g. *Salmonella typhi*, which causes typhoid fever. The first name may be contracted into Sal. or just S. One of the commonest of all is *S. typhi-murium*; the name suggests that it causes typhoid in mice (*mus*), though this is not correct. Another fairly common one is *S. cholerae-suis*; it causes a diarrhoeal disease in the pig (*sus*) but it is hardly correct to call this cholera, for that disease is caused by a germ of different family.

27

All this may seem to have very little to do with food poisoning, but when one is trying to get an exact picture of any problem, as we are of food poisoning, it is as well to use the terms exactly, and there is no harm in knowing what words mean. Perhaps we had better now have a closer look at the germs themselves.

Salmonellae

Salmonellae are short, thin, rod-like germs. They propel themselves along by means of fine threads or flagella which stream out from the sides of the rod and are in constant motion. Their appearance under the microscope is that of a very badly trained rowing eight, except that there are far more than eight pairs of oars or flagella, and the course steered is a very irregular one. The word flagella means whips, and flagella look more like twisting whips than rigid oars.

Individual salmonellae can be seen only under the microscope, but when they are grown on agar jelly they form colonies consisting of thousands of germs and these colonies are two to three millimetres in diameter and easily seen on the surface of the jelly. The salmonella family of germs is a very big one with over 1,000 different members. These salmonellae, although they share the main family features, all differ slightly from one another, and these differences can be detected by very sensitive laboratory tests. They are all given distinctive names as described above—*S. typhimurium*, *S. dublin*, *S. heidelberg* and so on.

Where salmonellae live

Salmonellae live as parasites in the intestinal canal of many different animals. They have been found in foxes, skunks, elephants, snakes, seals, quails, pigeons, tortoises and many others. They are very common parasites of farmyard fowls and animals, and it is from this source that they usually spread to man.

Salmonellae can survive in soil for a year, and for long periods in dust on floors and tables. They have been grown from the waste pipes of water-closets and of wash-hand-basins, especially in

28

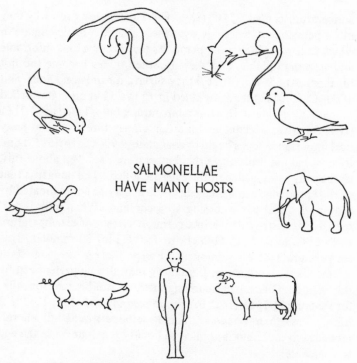

FIG. 3. Salmonellae often reach man from animals

bakeries and factories where contaminated food may be handled. They can be grown from swabs dipped in sewers into which the faeces of infected animals or humans is passed, and sewer swabs are sometimes used to trace the path of infection in outbreaks of disease. The ultimate source of salmonellae is always the intestinal canal of some animal, for it is only there that they can in nature flourish and multiply: but if they get into man's foodstuffs and are given the right conditions of temperature and moisture, they find things very much to their liking there too.

Effect of heat and cold

Temperature is very important. Salmonellae like the same body temperature as man, 37° C. (98·6° F.). This is one reason why they like a parasitic existence—it gives them a nice, equable climate in which to live. At higher temperatures they become uncomfortable and stop multiplying, and they die when things become too hot for them. At 55° C. (131° F.) they survive for only one hour, and at 60° C. (140° F.) they are killed in 15 to 20 minutes. One called *S. senftenberg* can survive this temperature, but is killed at 71·2° C. (160° F.) in a few seconds. This latter temperature is of great practical importance. Eggs begin to coagulate at 72° C. (161·6° F.) and in most baking procedures the temperature rises well above this, so that any salmonellae in the eggs are killed. (The danger is that cooked products, e.g. baked egg custard, may be contaminated by egg powder dust while cooling after cooking.) When milk is pasteurized to destroy dangerous germs, it is kept at a temperature of 62·6° C. to 65·5° C. (145° F. to 150° F.) for 30 minutes. This temperature kills all salmonellae except the rare heat-resistant strains like *S. senftenberg*. Liquid egg may also be pasteurized by this method. Quicker pasteurizing methods can be used for milk, for example 71·7° C. (161° F.) for 15 seconds or 132° C. (270° F.) for not less than 1 second. These methods would kill all salmonellae in milk, but if applied to liquid egg might cause the egg to coagulate.

Salmonellae, like most other micro-organisms, can withstand cold much better than heat. They stop multiplying at around 5° C. (41° F.). This is well above freezing-point which is 0° C. (32° F.). A domestic refrigerator need not have the temperature down to freezing-point to stop germs multiplying—a temperature around 5° C. (41° F.) is adequate. When a deep-freeze refrigerator is used to freeze and preserve food, the temperature falls far below freezing-point, but salmonellae in the food, for example inside a chicken, are not killed by this treatment. When the bird is thawed out and the temperature rises above 5° C. (41° F.) they begin to multiply again. It is important to remember that *refrigeration does not kill germs*.

Effect of moisture

Salmonellae, like other living things, need water. They can, however, survive for long periods in dry dust or in powder, but they cannot multiply in the absence of moisture. Salmonellae are often present in untreated dried-egg powder and they have occasionally been grown from dried milk. As soon as water is added to the powder and the temperature is right, the salmonellae start multiplying again till soon the liquid egg or the reconstituted milk is teeming with germs.

Effects of chemicals

Ordinary disinfectants such as the phenols kill salmonellae readily; these cannot be used on foodstuffs, but chlorine and potassium permanganate can. Lettuce can be rendered germ-free if immersed in water containing 80 parts per million of chlorine for 30 seconds; chicken carcasses need a concentration of 200 parts per million for 10 minutes. Antibiotics may also kill salmonellae if added to washing fluids or the slush ice used in poultry plants. The snag is that some salmonellae, resistant to antibiotics, may make their appearance; these can then flourish in spite of the antibiotic and lead to a very false sense of security.

Summary

Salmonellae are very common germs. They infect farm animals and this may lead to contamination of food. They are easily killed by heat. They are not killed by freezing or drying though they stop multiplying. Under certain conditions they multiply rapidly in human foodstuffs.

Shigellae

Shigellae are the germs which cause dysentery. Like salmonellae, they are short, rod-like germs. They form tiny colonies on special agar jelly which contains several sugars, including lactose. Most intestinal germs attack lactose and form acid from it and when this occurs an indicator in the jelly turns the colonies pink. Shigellae do not attack lactose and so their colonies remain white and can be easily distinguished from the other germs on the plate. They are known as non-lactose fermenters.

The shigella family is quite a small one and consists of just over 30 members—the salmonella family has more than 1,000 members. Three well-known members of the shigella family are *Shigella sonnei*, *Shigella flexneri* and *Shigella shigae*, all called after the doctors who first described them.

Where shigellae live

Shigellae live as parasites of the intestinal canal of man, and man is their only host: this is very different from the salmonellae which have very many hosts. If an outbreak of food-borne dysentery occurs, there must be somewhere in the chain of infection a human carrier of the germ, most probably in the kitchen.

This does not mean that shigellae cannot exist outside the human body. They certainly can, and often survive for long periods in dust, on tables, on cloths and even in sand. They like a warm, damp atmosphere in subdued light, and may linger for days in and around water-closets. Shigellae can live on the fingers for several hours and can pass from hand to hand very easily, and then from hand to mouth. This is the way dysentery usually spreads, from person to person, but if the germs do get into food, they multiply in it and outbreaks of dysentery have been caused in this way (p. 201).

Effect of heat and cold

Shigellae survive for long periods at room temperature and at body temperature, but they are readily destroyed by moderate heat, almost exactly the same as are salmonellae (p. 30). They survive freezing for weeks on end, so they are not killed by being placed in a refrigerator or a deep-freeze.

Effect of moisture

Like all germs, shigellae require moisture for multiplication, though they can get along in dry dust or on a piece of cloth for quite some time. They prefer conditions of high humidity, that is where there is a lot of moisture in the air.

Effect of chemicals

Shigellae are fairly easily killed by disinfectants. Phenol 1 per cent kills them in 15 minutes, and a solution of benzalkonium chloride 1 per cent in one minute; this latter can be used as a hand-washing solution during outbreaks of dysentery.

Summary

Shigellae are parasites of man only, and dysentery is usually spread by direct or indirect contact between human beings. If a carrier of shigellae is employed in the handling of food, shigellae may get into the food and then an outbreak of food-borne dysentery may follow.

Staphylococci

Staphylococci are rather stout, round germs which usually cluster together like bunches of grapes—*staphylococcus* means a bunch of grapes. Unlike the salmonellae they have no flagella or whips and so are non-motile. A single staphylococcus is invisible to the human eye, but can be seen easily under a low-power microscope lens. They form colonies readily on agar jelly and these look like tiny pieces of butter scattered on the surface of the jelly. Some of the colonies are coloured—white, yellow or gold—and, to some extent, this colour helps to identify the more dangerous germs. *Staphylococcus albus*, the white staphylococcus, is usually harmless, whereas the golden one, *Staphylococcus aureus*, is dangerous.

Staphylococci form a family of several hundred members, and it is important to be able to distinguish them one from another. This is done by exposing a staphylococcus to even smaller microorganisms known as phages. The word phage comes from the Greek word, *phagein*, meaning to eat, and these phages actually attack and destroy staphylococci. However they are very 'choosey':

one phage will attack only a few members of the staphylococcal family. Each phage is given a number, and a staphylococcus is known by the numbers of the phages that attack it. Thus staphylococcus phage type 6/47 is attacked by phages 6 and 47; staphylococcus 29/52/6/7/42E/47/54/73/75 is attacked by all the phages represented by these numbers. This typing is a piece of very skilled bacteriological technique, and fortunately the details do not concern us; but we must remember that, in the investigation of an outbreak of food poisoning, such typing is essential to ensure that no false trails are followed. It is quite common to find a staphylococcus on the hands or in the nose of a food handler, but one must know its phage type before one can say it is the same staphylococcus as caused the outbreak.

Not all staphylococci can cause food poisoning, but only those which produce an intestinal toxin called enterotoxin. It is this toxin which causes the vomiting and diarrhoea of food poisoning, not the staphylococci themselves.

Where staphylococci live

Staphylococci are parasites, and one of their commonest hosts is man. Over 50 per cent of normal people carry staphylococci in their nose and throat, and half of them have staphylococci on their hands as well. Not all these germs form enterotoxin, but possibly half of them do, so that at least 20 per cent of normal people carry food-poisoning staphylococci in their noses or on their hands. This means that if five people are employed in a kitchen, at least one of them is likely to be a carrier of these dangerous staphylococci. This does not mean that an outbreak of food poisoning is bound to follow. The germs have still got to get into the right type of food and be given the right conditions of temperature and moisture in order to multiply. It is only when multiplying that staphylococci produce enterotoxin. Food hygiene consists in preventing germs getting on to food, or of multiplying if they do.

Staphylococci, although essentially parasites of man and animals, can exist outside the body and may be grown from towels, tables, knives, dishes or anything that a carrier touches. They may

34

be grown from the air or dust in a contaminated kitchen or bake-house. Flies in such an environment readily become infected and may carry the germs on their feet, or their mouthparts, or in their intestines and infect food if they alight on it.

Staphylococci are often present in cowsheds and can easily get into milk. They sometimes cause an inflammation of the udder in cattle, and then the milk may be teeming with staphylococci. Sometimes the staphylococci are the food-poisoning type and, as the germs multiply rapidly in milk, anyone drinking the milk raw may get food poisoning. Pasteurization of milk kills staphylococci so that pasteurized milk is safe milk.

Effect of heat and cold

Staphylococci are killed by heating to 60° C. (140° F.) for 30 minutes. This is well below cooking temperatures so that staphylococci will not survive cooking, provided the heat penetrates the food: this is not always the case inside a pie or large joint. Staphylococci grow rapidly at warm room-temperature, especially in food, and, as they multiply, they produce enterotoxin. This toxin withstands boiling for 30 minutes, so that even if contaminated food is reheated before being eaten, the toxin is probably not destroyed and food poisoning may follow. The food in such a case is sterile, because all the staphylococci are dead, but the toxin is still there. This is why, in some outbreaks of staphylococcal food poisoning, staphylococci may not be found in specimens taken from patients: dead germs cannot come to life again in the laboratory.

Staphylococci multiply rapidly in warm milk; after a few hours standing at around 35° C. (95° F.) milk may be teeming with them: but, under modern conditions, milk is cooled quickly after being drawn and staphylococci have little chance to grow. In the early stages of cheese-making, staphylococci find temperatures much to their liking and they can outgrow the germs which are used to 'start' the cheese: but if cheese is made from pasteurized milk, as in all modern cheese factories, there is no danger, for any staphylococci present are killed.

Staphylococci are not killed by freezing: they may survive for months in the frozen state, though they cannot multiply. This is important in the making of ice-cream: if staphylococci have been allowed to grow and produce toxin when the mix was warm, the freezing will not make the ice-cream safe to eat.

Effect of moisture

Staphylococci cannot multiply in the absence of moisture. On the other hand they can stay alive for months in the dried state. They might for example survive for months in dried-egg or milk powder, and when the powder is reconstituted by the addition of water the staphylococci could begin to multiply again and produce enterotoxin.

Effects of chemicals

Salts such as nitrates and nitrites used in curing hams and other foods do not kill staphylococci: nor does pickling, for staphylococci can live in 10 per cent solution of salt. Antibiotics do kill staphylococci, especially penicillin, but staphylococci often become resistant to them. Ordinary disinfectants such as phenol are not very effective against staphylococci, which, however, are readily killed by the aniline dye disinfectants.

Summary

Staphylococci are common germs, often present on the hands or in the noses of normal people. Some types produce an enterotoxin, and this may cause food poisoning. Staphylococci are killed by ordinary cooking temperatures, but the enterotoxin survives boiling.

Clostridium welchii

Clostridium welchii is one of the spore-bearing germs. It is rod-shaped with parallel sides, but when conditions prevent it from multiplying, the rod becomes swollen just short of the end. This swelling is the spore.

Where Clostridium welchii lives

Clostridium welchii is primarily a native of the soil, whence it probably gets on to vegetables and other foodstuffs and is swallowed by man and animals. It is a common inhabitant of the intestinal tract and probably many normal persons have the germ in their bowels and excrete it in their faeces: in residential institutions, with communal cooking, most of the inhabitants may do so. Nearly 20 per cent of pigs harbour the germ, and the same percentage of rats and mice. It is not so common in cattle, probably in less than 2 per cent. The germ may be found in dust, water, milk and sewage. In fact, it is found almost anywhere, in the dust and air of kitchens, bakeries and shops. Flies and bluebottles are often heavily infected with *Clostridium welchii* and so spread it to food. Swabs of the surface of raw meat are positive in 25 per cent of cases.

A very important point is that this germ does not grow willingly in the presence of air; it likes a situation where the amount of oxygen is reduced. It is, therefore, an anaerobic germ. It does not multiply on the surface of raw meat, but if it can find its way into the depths of a luke-warm stew, it finds ideal conditions of warmth and low oxygen, and so it multiplies rapidly and produces toxin. To produce food poisoning the food must contain live clostridia and the toxin, not, as is the case with staphylococci, the toxin only. The presence of spores may also be necessary: these may germinate in the body after being swallowed and produce some poisonous substance in man's intestinal canal.

Effect of heat and cold

The non-sporing or vegetative form of the germ is readily killed by ordinary cooking temperatures. Spores can resist boiling for hours on end. Well-cooked meat may still contain live spores. As the meat cools, the spores germinate and produce the vegetative germs. These begin to multiply round about 50° C. (122° F.) and, if the meat is allowed to cool slowly, it may be heavily infected with clostridia by the time the temperature reaches 20° C. (68° F.).

All this time the multiplying germs are producing toxin. If the contaminated food is now put in a refrigerator, multiplication stops, but the germ remains alive and the toxin remains toxic. Toxin is not destroyed by boiling, so that if the meat is re-heated next day before being eaten, it will still be full of active toxin, and food poisoning may follow, especially if some spores are also present (p. 37).

When meat is cooked some hours before being served, it is often kept on a hot plate or in a *bain marie* till it is eaten. Such conditions are ideal for the multiplication of *Clostridium welchii*. If food is not to be served immediately after cooking, it must either (*a*) be cooked rapidly, put in a refrigerator overnight and be quickly re-heated next day or (*b*) it must be kept at a temperature well above 60° C. till it is served. Otherwise there is a danger of food poisoning.

Effect of moisture

The germs can grow only in the presence of moisture. Spores can survive dryness for very long periods.

Effect of chemicals

The vegetative form of *Clostridium welchii* is killed readily by ordinary disinfectants and by penicillin. The spores are very resistant to disinfectants and to penicillin.

Summary

Clostridium welchii is a spore-bearing germ. The spore withstands boiling. The vegetative form is destroyed by cooking, but in warm food it multiplies rapidly and produces toxin. Cooked food must therefore be kept very hot, or cooled very quickly to prevent the germ multiplying.

Clostridium botulinum

This germ belongs to the same group of germs as *Clostridium welchii* and is like it in its appearance under the microscope. It is also a spore-bearer. There are at least 6 main members of the

Clostridium botulinum family, lettered A to F. Most illnesses in man are caused by types A, B and E. The toxins produced by each type differ slightly from one another, but each toxin has a very similar and very powerful effect on the human body. The illness is very different from other forms of food poisoning and is often fatal (see Chapter 4).

Where Clostridium botulinum lives

Clostridium botulinum lives only in soil or on decaying vegetation, not in living animals. It is a saprophyte, not a parasite: *sapro* comes from the Greek word, *sapros*, meaning rottenness, and *phyte* means 'living on'. It is a very strict anaerobe and will not grow in ordinary atmospheric air. It may be present on vegetables and other fresh food, but does not multiply there and so does not produce toxin. Such food is therefore harmless. When food is preserved by pickling, or smoking or canning, the amount of oxygen is reduced, and if *Clostridium botulinum* survived the preserving process, it could begin to multiply and produce the toxin in the food. If this food were then eaten uncooked, fatal botulism would follow, for the toxin is exceedingly powerful, and even a taste can kill. Fortunately *Clostridium botulinum* is nearly always killed in commercial preservation, but it can survive faulty home-canning.

Effect of heat and cold

Three things must be considered—the vegetative or multiplying germ, the spore and the toxin. The vegetative form of the germ is killed at 80° C. (176° F.), a higher temperature than is necessary for salmonellae or staphylococci, but still well below boiling-point and the temperature reached in canning. Spores are very resistant to heat. Type A spores resist boiling for hours, but are killed in 5 minutes at 121° C. (250° F.): the other types (B to F) are slightly easier to kill. Commercial methods of canning are adjusted to these temperatures: steam under pressure is required. Botulinum toxin is destroyed quite easily by heat: all forms are killed in 2 minutes at temperatures below boiling-point. The toxins of types

39

A, B and E (those that cause illness in man) are killed in 2 minutes at between 60° C. and 70° C. (140° F. to 158° F.), well below boiling-point: types C and D require 80° C. (176° F.), while type F is destroyed at temperatures not much over 37° C. (98·6° F.). Clearly then, if food is preserved at the correct high temperatures, spores are killed and the food is safe: but even if some spores survive, multiply in food and form toxin, this toxin would be destroyed quickly if the food were heated above 80° C. (176° F.), and the food could then be eaten without causing botulism. However, if the food were eaten without being heated, then all who ate it would get the disease, and most of them would die. *Clostridium botulinum* is a common germ of the soil, but cases of botulism are rare.

The germs survive freezing. All the vegetative forms, except type E, stop multiplying under 5° C. (41° F.) but begin to multiply again above that temperature. Type E is a little more resistant to cold. Spores and toxin survive freezing indefinitely, and any spores or toxin present in food when it is put into deep-freeze, will still be present when it is taken out.

Effect of moisture

Clostridium botulinum requires moisture for growth, but spores survive for years in dry dust.

Effect of chemicals

The acidity of food has a marked effect on the survival of *Clostridium botulinum*. When this is round about neutral point, pH 7·0, spores resist boiling for hours: in more acid foods, around pH 5·0, the same spores are killed by boiling in 45 minutes, while in very acid foods, around pH 3·5, boiling kills them in 10 minutes. Vinegar in a concentration of 2 per cent destroys the spores, as does salt at 8 to 10 per cent.

All this is very important and explains why the germ is killed by some preserving methods in which the temperature is too low to do so. Tinned fruit, for example, is an acid product, and botulism has never been caused by eating it. String beans, on the other hand, seem to favour the growth of the germ, and botulism has been caused by eating home-canned beans. All the factors affecting the growth and destruction of *Clostridium botulinum* are not fully understood and constant watch must be kept on changing methods and changing fashions in food production and consumption, lest some minor alteration in the environment around the germ lead to its unexpected survival in the food. The 'pasteurization' of canned hams (p. 170) for example, must be carefully controlled.

Summary

Clostridium botulinum is a spore-bearing, toxin-producing germ. It is often present in soil. It grows only in low concentrations of oxygen. The spores are very heat-resistant, but the toxin, although a very powerful one, is destroyed by heat.

Vibrio parahaemolyticus

This is a small germ in spite of its big name. It is one of the halophilic germs. This name comes from the Greek words *hal* for salt and *philein* meaning to love. So it is a salt-loving germ and is found in sea water, usually in warm coastal waters. It is common in the Far East, especially in Japan, where it has often caused food poisoning, but it has been found in coastal waters in many other parts of the world, even where the water is not so warm, as around Canada, Holland and Britain.

The germ gets into fish and shellfish, and if the infected fish is eaten this can cause food poisoning in man. Usually this occurs in the warmest months of the year, and in Japan this type of food poisoning is often caused by eating raw fish dishes. No cooking and warmth cause germs to multiply.

Food poisoning by *Vibrio parahaemolyticus* has never been reported in Britain before 1973, but that year some passengers on an aeroplane from Bangkok to London ate some seafood during the flight and developed vomiting and diarrhoea after arrival in Britain. The same happened in 1974: again seafood eaten during a flight from Bangkok caused food poisoning among passengers after arrival in Britain. In both instances the germ was *Vibrio parahaemolyticus*.

So far no food poisoning of this type has occurred from eating seafood served in Britain, though the germ has been grown from fish caught in British waters. Possibly the temperature is too low in Britain for the germ to multiply freely and our methods of cooking kill the germs before they can harm us. The germ does not produce a food poisoning toxin like the Staphylococcus (p. 33), so if the germ is killed there is nothing to cause food poisoning. But things keep changing in the world of germs as in the world of man. Man often changes his food habits: this salt-loving germ might take advantage of any such change.

Bacillus cereus

This is a common germ. It can be found in dust, soil and on green vegetables and potatoes. It likes to grow where there is plenty of air but it can grow even where there is little air or oxygen. It likes warmth: a temperature of around 35° C. (95° F.) suits it best, but it can grow at temperatures between 10° C. (50° F.) and 45° C. (113° F.). So it is a very adaptable germ and it is surprising that it is only recently that it has been known to cause food poisoning in Britain.

Since 1971 there have been several outbreaks, most often caused by eating fried rice in Chinese restaurants. The rice had usually been boiled the day before it was required, and left in a warm room overnight: this would allow germs to get on the food and to multiply quickly. Next day it was gently fried before serving to customers, too gently to kill *Bacillus cereus*. Other outbreaks have been caused by eating meat loaf and some sauces. Always there is a long delay between preparing and serving the food, a common factor in food poisoning outbreaks.

Some Definitions

Micro-organism—a germ

Vegetative state—the state of an actively growing, actively multiplying germ. Usually easily destroyed by heat or chemicals: may produce toxin

Spore—the 'sleeping form' of a germ. Highly resistant to heat, cold, drying and chemicals. Spores do not multiply but, when conditions are favourable, they germinate into the vegetative state

Toxin—a chemical substance produced by rapidly growing germs. Usually poisonous to man

Aerobe—a germ which grows in ordinary air

Anaerobe—a germ which grows only where oxygen concentration is low

Pathogen—a disease-producing germ

Non-pathogenic—not capable of producing disease

4

Food Poisoning and Botulism: Clinical Aspects

The term 'food poisoning' has an alarming ring about it. People don't get very worried about an attack of enteritis or diarrhoea: they accept it as almost a normal incident: but the term 'food poisoning' is dramatic and frightening. Yet, in most cases, food poisoning is simply a form of enteritis conveyed by food, and there is no need for patients to be unduly anxious. The term 'food poisoning' is a useful one, because it emphasizes the fact that food is to blame. Caterers, cooks and all who handle food should certainly be worried and alarmed by outbreaks of food poisoning, for it is a condition which is preventable and therefore should never occur.

Incubation period

This is the time that passes between the entry of the germ or toxin into the body and the occurrence of the first symptom. In staphylococcal cases, the toxin is present in the food and it irritates the stomach very quickly: the incubation period is therefore short, usually from $\frac{1}{2}$ hour to 4 or 5 hours. In salmonella poisoning there is no toxin: the germs need time to multiply in the patient's intestinal tract and cause symptoms only when they reach very high numbers: the incubation period is therefore longer, from 12 to 48 hours. In *Clostridium welchii* poisoning, toxin is present but the germs also multiply inside the patient: the incubation period is between 12 to 24 hours. None of these figures is exact. A good deal depends on how heavily infected the food is: if there are very large numbers of salmonellae, for example, the incubation period might be only 8 to 12 hours, but a very short incubation period usually means staphylococcal poisoning.

Symptoms

There are three symptoms common to all three forms—diarrhoea, vomiting and pain. The incidence in the three forms of food poisoning is different.

Salmonella food poisoning. Diarrhoea is the main symptom. It varies in severity. In most patients it is moderately severe, with diarrhoea occurring every hour or so at the start but usually ceasing after the first day. In some it is much more severe and causes collapse, while in others it amounts to nothing more than a few loose stools which the patient hardly notices. At the onset the patient may have a little griping, abdominal pain but this is never severe. Vomiting is uncommon except when the food has been very heavily contaminated. The whole illness is usually over within two days, though the patient may continue to pass salmonellae in his faeces for much longer.

Sometimes salmonellae get through into the patient's bloodstream and the illness is then much more severe and requires specialized treatment. Such a patient can be ill for several weeks, and the germ may settle down in some part of the body, especially the bone marrow, and cause internal abscesses many years later. This invasion of the blood-stream depends partly on the amount of infection in the food, but much more on the type of salmonella. *S. cholerae-suis* and *S. virchow* are two types which can cause this type of illness.

Staphylococcal food poisoning. The most prominent symptom is vomiting. This is due to the toxin irritating the lining of the stomach. It is sometimes very severe and can lead to very great weakness or collapse. The vomiting helps to get rid of some of the toxin and this helps to cut the illness short. Vomiting usually stops within 5 to 6 hours but the patient may feel exhausted for the next 12 hours. Pain is not common, other than that caused by the vomiting. Diarrhoea is usually not severe and many patients have none at all.

Clostridium welchii food poisoning. Pain in the abdomen is common. It can be fairly severe at first, a nagging, colicky pain in the upper abdomen and may last for several hours. It is followed by mild diarrhoea in nearly all patients. Vomiting is uncommon. The illness is usually over in one or two days.

It will be seen, then, that the three types of illness differ a little in their symptoms. If most of the patients in an outbreak complain mainly of abdominal pain, the cause is probably *Clostridium welchii.* If vomiting is their main symptom, the cause is probably staphylococcal. If diarrhoea, with little pain or vomiting, is prominent, the outbreak may be due to salmonellae.

In all three forms, the illness is, on the whole, sharp but short. In a few patients, especially frail old patients or patients already ill with another disease, it can be very severe or even fatal.

The illnesses caused by *Vibrio parahaemolyticus* and *Bacillus cereus* usually consist of diarrhoea and vomiting. These symptoms have varied a bit in their times of onset in different outbreaks. The nature of the infection can be diagnosed only in the laboratory.

Laboratory diagnosis

An exact diagnosis can be made only by bacteriological tests. Specimens of vomit, faeces and blood from the patient and any portions of the food should be sent to the laboratory. These specimens will be put into special media, see Chapter 2, and the bacteriologist will carry out tests to identify and type the germs. All this takes time and it may be several days or more than a week before the final result is known. A preliminary report can often be given in 24 hours and this usually gives an accurate enough clue to those who are investigating the outbreak. When the outbreak is a staphylococcal one, the results are often negative: this is because the staphylococci themselves have been killed in cooking, and so do not grow in the laboratory; tests for the toxin can be carried out but they are complicated.

46

Botulism

Botulism is a disease with symptoms very different from the above forms of food poisoning. Its main effect is to cause paralysis of muscles by blocking the nervous impulses to them. It very often causes death. Fortunately it is a rare disease.

Incubation period

The toxin is already present in the food when swallowed and it rapidly passes through the wall of the stomach and into the bloodstream which carries it to nerve-endings in muscles. The incubation period is commonly between 10 and 12 hours: it may be shorter or longer, probably depending on the amount of toxin in the food.

Symptoms

The first symptoms are those of vague discomfort and weakness. Soon signs of paralysis occur. The first is blurring of vision due to weakness of the muscles that help the eyes to focus. Next drooping of the eyelids occurs and difficulty in speaking. The muscles of the throat are soon affected and the patient becomes unable to swallow even his own saliva. The breathing muscles become paralysed, and the condition now is one of great distress. The patient's brain remains clear and he is fully aware of his desperate plight. From now on the course is rapidly downhill. Very few, if any, who reach this stage recover, but some patients, who have eaten very little of the food, escape with mild attacks.

Diagnosis

If several patients fall ill at the same time with these symptoms, the diagnosis of botulism is obvious, for there is no other illness capable of causing simultaneous and rapid paralysis in a group of people. If there is only one patient, it is difficult to diagnose, for many other illnesses can produce solitary cases of paralysis. Specimens of vomit, faeces and of food are examined in the laboratory.

47

The germs may grow on special media, and the presence of toxin may be shown by injecting extracts of the food into mice.

Dysentery

Dysentery is not typically food borne, but occasionally it can be. The symptoms may be indistinguishable from those of salmonella food poisoning. There is diarrhoea, some abdominal pain and sometimes vomiting. Shigellae sometimes cause ulceration of the bowel wall, and when this occurs there may be bleeding from the bowel. Usually this is very slight for most cases of dysentery are mild; sometimes the attack is severe and the patient suffers greatly from loss of blood. A good deal depends on which germ causes the infection; *Shigella sonnei* causes mild illnesses, whereas *Shigella shigae* tends to cause severe attacks.

There are many other illnesses which can be conveyed by food. Typhoid fever, brucellosis (Malta fever), and infectious hepatitis (jaundice) are examples (see Chapter 10), but these are not included under the term food poisoning. The food handler should know of their existence. The methods of preventing food poisoning will also prevent these other diseases from being conveyed by food.

How common is food poisoning? Botulism at any rate is rare. Very few doctors see a case in the whole of their professional lives. So the risk is minute, but the people who handle food must know that the risk exists, and constant watch must be kept on the methods of food production, especially canning, to make sure that no fault creeps in. Food poisoning caused by *Vibrio parahaemolyticus* and *Bacillus cereus* have not so far been common in Britain but these 'new' germs must be carefully watched: we know something about them now. The other forms of food poisoning are common, and most people suffer at least one attack in their lives, even if it is not recognized as such. People talk of a 'tummy upset' (horrible phrase) caused by 'something I've eaten'. Usually this is food poisoning, and it is caused by something they should not have been required to eat.

5

The Trail of Infection

Infection on the Farm

There is no such thing as natural methods of farming, for farming is fundamentally an unnatural process. It consists of controlling the growth of plants and animals, encouraging any features that promise a good return in the market, and pruning out any that are likely to be unprofitable. Animals that in nature would roam widely in search of food and mates are, on farms, confined to fields or locked in buildings, their reproduction regulated by artificial insemination and their milk production controlled by dairy requirements. Nothing could be less 'natural' for a cow than life on a dairy farm, or for a calf than existence in an intensive calf-rearing unit. A cowshed is not the natural environment for the cow, nor a deep-litter shed for a hen. Yet under these unnatural conditions the animals thrive, for they get more food, water and shelter than they could obtain in the wild state, but if some foreign disease-germ breaks in, the artificial surroundings of their domesticated reserve at once become highly dangerous.

Animals defaecate and urinate where they stand, and no matter how well washed and clean a cowshed may be, the floors, the bedding, the stalls and the walls can never be sterile. There must always be a warm, moist film of organic material on all surfaces, and pathogenic germs can flourish in such conditions. The very processes of cleaning with brushes and water may stir this material up and cause an invisible mist of infectious material in the atmosphere. Soon the cowshed can be a very dangerous place for the cows. Germs may settle on their foodstuff or be present in the air they breathe. Shortly some of the animals sicken, and a sick

49

animal in turn passes the germ in its faeces, urine, breath or milk and so adds to the weight of infection in the cowshed.

Source of infection

In animal, as in human outbreaks of disease it is always difficult to determine how the infecting germ gets into a community: once it is in, it is much easier to trace its spread. There are two main avenues of infection on farms; one is the introduction of new animals, and the other is artificial foodstuffs.

Animal carriers

Cattle. When a cow is infected with a salmonella, it may suffer from severe diarrhoea or have a vague feverish illness. This is often called 'cattle paratyphoid', but it is not caused by *Salmonella paratyphi*, which causes paratyphoid in man; the usual cause is *Salmonella dublin*. Some cows die of 'cattle paratyphoid' but most recover: though they become perfectly fit again, they continue to pass the germs in their faeces, often for the rest of their lives. In other words, the animal becomes a carrier: a carrier excretes the germ, but suffers no ill effects from it after the original illness. It is, however, a great danger to other animals. If such a cow is bought at market and added to a 'clean' herd, it will sooner or later cause infection in the other animals.

Calves also suffer from salmonella infection, usually in short, sharp epidemics. Under intensive methods of stock farming, calves from hundreds of different farms may be brought together in one unit for rearing. The calves are separated from their dams a few hours to a few days after birth. They are taken in trucks to markets or dealers' premises and the trucks pick up calves from other farms on the way. They are then sold to rearing farms where they are kept for varying periods. Some rearers move them at three months to other farms for fattening, others keep them till they are slaughtered at 12 to 15 months old. An intensive calf-farming unit of 500 calves may get its stock from over 400 different farms so that a great deal of mixing takes place. Obviously, if a few calves arrive in an infectious state the infection can spread rapidly. The illness is usually milder than in adult cows and the calves do not become permanent carriers, but excrete the germ for only a few weeks, but sometimes the infection takes a more severe form and many calves die. If the germ is *Salmonella dublin* the origin of the infection is probably an adult cow on one of the farms, for *Salmonella dublin* is a parasite mainly of cattle. If another salmonella is the cause, say *Salmonella typhimurium*, then the infection may have come from other sources—rats, fowls or feeding stuffs—for *Salmonella typhimurium* infects many different hosts.

Pigs. All the above relates to cattle, but other animals on the farm suffer similar infections. Pigs are very often infected with salmonellae: the pig is the main host of *Salmonella cholerae-suis*, but it is often infected with other salmonellae as well, such as *Salmonella typhimurium* and *Salmonella dublin*. Pigs very readily infect one another and the germ, after the acute attack, settles down in the abdominal glands of the pig and is often still present there when the animal is slaughtered for food.

Sheep. Sheep are much less often infected with salmonellae. They live out in the open, instead of in cowsheds or sties, so that the germs have less chance of building up a heavy load of infection in the environment. But salmonellae can live in soil and pasture: they have been grown from cow-dung that has lain for 9 months in a field.

Poultry. Farmyard fowls are often heavily infected. They have two salmonellae of their own, *Salmonella pullorum* and *Salmonella gallinarum*, and these have very seldom caused infection in man. Fowls may, however, be infected with many other salmonellae. Often they show no sign of illness but can still spread the infection to other animals on the farm. Hens, ducks, geese and turkeys may all be infected. The salmonellae are often still present in the carcass of fowls when killed for food, and if the bird is not properly cooked, those who eat it may get food poisoning (p. 193).

Rats and mice. Rats and mice become heavily infected if there are salmonellae on the farm and they can spread the infection by contaminating feeding stuffs, bedding and drinking water. However, they are really the victims, not the cause of the infection, and

THE TRAIL OF INFECTION

if the farm is cleaned up and infected stock animals removed, the infection dies out in the rats and mice, but it is obviously better to get rid of the rats and mice too.

Dogs and cats. Dogs and cats wander round farm buildings and pick up and eat all kinds of infected material. They may become infected with salmonellae and then carry the infection into the farmhouse and infect the family. A member of the family may become a carrier, and he or she can spread the infection, and perhaps contaminate milk or other farm products. It is not a common occurrence, but outbreaks have been caused in this way.

Feeding stuffs. Feeding stuffs are supplied usually as meal or pellets, and always contain animal protein. This protein comes from the carcasses of dead animals and these animals may have been infected with salmonellae before death. If so, the germs survive in the feeding stuffs and are conveyed to other animals, perhaps across an ocean, for much animal feeding stuff is imported. As much as 15 to 45 per cent of artificial feeding stuffs has been found to be infected with salmonellae. Man is not the only animal that suffers from food infections: the animals which are fed on these feeding stuffs are subjected to a compulsory form of food poisoning. There is no excuse for this, for there is no difficulty, except a commercial one, in sterilizing feeding stuffs before they go on the market.

All the above has dealt with salmonella infection on the farm. Staphylococcal infection of milk is another hazard on the farm, although a minor one. It is dealt with in a later chapter (p. 103).

Not hot-beds of infection

It would be wrong to give the impression that stock farms are hot-beds of infection. This is far from being true. Animals on most farms are healthy and free of infection, and when they leave the farm for the market and beyond, they are usually in good condition; but their journey onwards from the farm is a hazardous one. The dangers they encounter are discussed in the next chapter.

6

The Trail of Infection

Animals on the Move

Crowd diseases

Epidemiology is the study of crowd diseases. The word comes from the Greek, *epi* which means upon, and *demos* meaning the people or the crowd, so that an epidemic is something that falls upon the crowd. Very often the crowd is on the move, and the histories of wars, migrations and pilgrimages are always also the histories of great epidemics or plagues that fell upon the moving crowd. Pilgrimages to Mecca, the Crusades, Napoleon's retreat from Moscow and the First and Second World Wars all provide examples, and the numbers dying of epidemic diseases often out-number those killed in battle. The reason is, of course, that when men travel rough, living standards fall: feeding facilities are im-provised and sanitary hygiene is primitive. Moreover, the men are exposed to great stresses and strains: they become over-tired and dispirited and, if infection breaks out, they are less able to resist it in their weakened state.

Stress and shrinkage

Animals on the move suffer too. When they leave the farm they may be driven on the hoof for long distances, or be huddled to-gether in lorries or train trucks for hours on end. Perhaps they are not fed and watered properly, and they must suffer from excite-ment and fear. When they reach the market, they are driven into pens and later into sale-rings, where they are paraded and prodded before auctioneer and farmers. All this produces *stress*, a word used by vets to describe the strains which cause animals to lose

FIG. 4. Animals on the move suffer from stress

condition while on the move. Farmers refer to *shrinkage*. This means the loss of weight which occurs in their animals between the farm and the sale-ring, a matter of commercial concern. Even under the best conditions of transport, the animals obviously suffer. How do they fare from infection?

FIG. 5. Stress leads to shrinkage in the sale-ring

From farm to market

When a truck leaves the first farm it may have only a few healthy animals on board. It stops at other farms on the way, loading a few more at each stop. Most of these also are healthy, but one or two may be infected. By the end of the journey the truck is soiled with faeces, the animals have been badly jostled, and any germs that are present in one animal have had every chance to spread to the others.

At the market other trucks are arriving, bringing cattle, sheep and pigs from farms scattered far and wide. The animals are unloaded and herded into pens and lairs in the market buildings where they may spend hours or days before being moved on to new farms, or to the abattoir. The bedding, the floors, walls and partitions are spattered with dung and urine, the temperature is warm and the atmosphere moist. The conditions are ideal for the multiplication and spread of germs. It is not a pretty picture, but the spread of infection never is.

Once walls and floors and partitions are contaminated it is not easy to make them free of germs. If these structures become caked with animal faeces, salmonellae and other germs can live almost indefinitely. To prevent this, absolute cleanliness with adequate and frequent hosing is required, but often not provided, and pens and lairs, as distinct from farms, may become hot-beds of infection. Animals coming into them have little chance of avoiding infection. Many investigations have been carried out by bacteriologists to show that infection spreads in this way, and that the longer the animals are held in such pens and lairs, the greater is the rise in infection.

At the abattoir

Animals arrive at the abattoir direct from farms, from markets where they have been sold for slaughter, or in ships from overseas. They are led into pens in buildings called lairages, there to await their final journey to the adjoining abattoir floor. In the pens they are exposed to the same danger of infection as in the markets, and if the lairages are badly managed, animals can become infected in their last few days of life. Even after slaughter the danger is not past, for clean carcasses can be contaminated with germs from the carcasses of infected animals. The slaughter-house side of an abattoir is often heavily contaminated with germs, and salmonellae have been grown from floors, dehairing machines, knives, chain tackle, trolleys, trucks and table-tops. It is easy to see how germs can spread under such circumstances, and a side of beef from an animal that was clean and healthy on the farm may leave the abattoir covered with pathogenic germs it has collected on the way.

Poultry plants

Hens, ducks, geese and turkeys go to poultry plants instead of abattoirs. They undergo similar stresses and probably greater chances of infection on the way, but they are not held, like the animals, in lairs before slaughter. At the poultry plant they are quickly killed, bled, defeathered, eviscerated, trussed and packed, all on a conveyor belt system. Along the line, contamination may build up anywhere and germs can be grown from evisceration and giblet troughs, chilling tanks and rinsing water: they can usually be grown from the floor and from drain swabs. Most important of all, disease germs may be present in the trussed fowl, either because the bird was already infected before slaughter or because the carcass has been contaminated on the way through the plant.

It is a long story from the entry of the germ into a farm to the exit of contaminated food from an abattoir or poultry plant, but germs have a tenacious hold on life and can adapt themselves to many changes of environment. Given favourable conditions they can survive on dead meat for long periods and, given a little warmth and moisture, they can soon multiply and be ready to take up a new parasitic existence inside the body of the human being who swallows them in his food.

It must not be thought that every market, every abattoir and every poultry plant is filthy and full of disease germs. This is far from true. A modern abattoir or poultry plant can be as clean as an operating theatre, and many are; but others fall far short of this standard. Moreover, cleanliness is not the same thing as asepsis or freedom from germs. Disease germs spread even in operating theatres. In the production of our foodstuffs there are unpleasant facts to face. Facing these facts is the purpose of this book.

7

The Trail of Infection

From Abattoir to Factory

Few of us ever see the inside of an abattoir or poultry plant, and most of us never think of it, but we are all familiar with the products—the side of beef, the joint, the chicken or the turkey. All this is normally very wholesome food, but, as we have seen, this kind of food is attractive not only to man, but to microbes. What happens when carcasses of animals or birds leave the abattoir or poultry plant contaminated with disease germs?

Meat factories

Sausages. The fate of a germ that enters a meat factory on a side of beef depends on the processes carried out there. If sausages are produced, the meat is chopped up and put in a mixing machine to which meal and spices are added. The sausage meat coming out of the mixer is then fed into a filling machine and sausages emerge from the other side. These are then carried on conveyor belts to a packing machine where the sausages are enclosed in Cellophane packets, untouched by human hands. The whole process can be very clean, but the danger of infection is unseen. If the surface of any carcass meat from the abattoir is contaminated with salmonellae, these germs are thoroughly spread around in the mixing process. All the plant becomes contaminated, and sausages made from wholesome meat are liable to contain salmonellae by the time they reach the packing machine. Moreover, the salmonellae are now *inside* the sausages, not just on the surface. This is important, for in lightly fried sausages the centre may easily not reach a high enough temperature to kill salmonellae. Salmonellae have,

57

in fact, survived in the centre of sausages gently fried for 15 minutes. It has been calculated that about 4 per cent of sausages sold in Britain contain salmonellae. This is a low percentage, but as around 9,000 million are sold every year, it represents a lot of sausages. They should all be browned on both sides.

Cooked meat. Often joints of meat or pork are roasted in meat factories and sent out cooked to wholesalers and retailers. Such meat may be contaminated when it arrives from the abattoir, but the germs, being surface germs, are sure to be killed in the roasting. The danger is that tables and other surfaces in the factory may be contaminated with salmonellae from the raw meat. If meat is placed on these after cooking, it can pick up some of these germs and, if the temperature is right, they can multiply on the surface of the cooked meat and eventually be swallowed by unfortunate consumers. This is not a theoretical risk, but one of the fundamental dangers of bulk food production. *Raw and cooked food should never be handled on the same surfaces.*

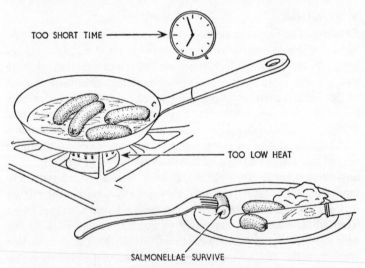

TOO SHORT TIME

TOO LOW HEAT

SALMONELLAE SURVIVE

FIG. 6. Salmonellae can survive gentle frying *inside* sausages; brown them well on both sides

Pies. Pies are often made in the same factory as sausages and the same risks are incurred, for any germs on the *surface* of abattoir meat are tucked well inside the *centre* of a pie. In a good modern food factory this should not matter, for the pies are cooked in magnificent automatic ovens in which thorough heat penetration can be guaranteed, and the pies are sterile when they come out at the other end; but in smaller factories or cook-shops the pies are sometimes cooked in wretched old ovens in which there may be cool spots where the temperature cannot be guaranteed. Most of the pies are sterile, but, in a few, some salmonellae escape, and these later find a cool pie an ideal place in which to settle down and multiply. Another danger is that agar jelly or gelatin is often added to pies after cooking. This is meant to represent the 'goodness' of the pie, though it usually contains little or no food value at all. Agar jelly and gelatin are both used in laboratories as media for growing germs, so it is not surprising that salmonellae, staphylococci or other germs, if they get into the pies at this stage, grow very readily in the jelly. In a good modern factory, the jelly is added via a sterile jelly gun, but in less up-to-date premises it may be poured into the pie from some far from sterile jug.

Glazes and tongues. A similar hazard attends the glazing of liver *pâtés* and similar meat products. The meat part is made sterile by cooking, but the gelatin glaze is sometimes kept tepid in a container till required. Germs can flourish in this liquid medium, and when the glaze is applied to the meat they readily invade it and multiply rapidly. To prevent this, the glaze or gelling should be prepared fresh each day and boiled for at least 5 minutes. It should be kept, while being used, at a temperature of at least 72° C. (161·6° F.). Any not used should be cooled rapidly and kept all night in a refrigerator, and boiled again next day, but it is much better to throw away any surplus glaze (p. 207).

Tongues must be partially cooked before they can be skinned. This involves handling, and germs can easily be added at this stage. The skinning should be done with the tongues as hot as can be borne, and the cooking completed immediately after, so that any added germs are killed before they have time to multiply. The tongues can then be cooked and pressed in sterile containers (p. 196).

Poultry barbecues

Hens, ducks, geese and turkeys are often heavily infected with salmonellae, but food poisoning outbreaks from eating poultry used to be uncommon in Britain. This was because birds had usually been bought fresh and cooked in the oven in the home. Fashions change in cooking as in other things, and this has been especially the case with poultry, especially chicken. The carcasses, instead of being sold fresh, are now often deep-frozen, and sent in the frozen

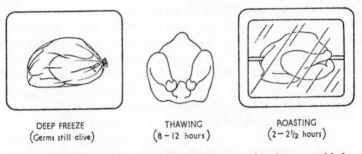

DEEP FREEZE
(Germs still alive)

THAWING
(8 – 12 hours)

ROASTING
(2 – 2½ hours)

FIG. 7. Deep-freezing does not kill germs. Roasting does, provided the bird is thoroughly thawed first so that the heat can penetrate the carcass

state direct to retailer or restaurants. It is important to recall that *freezing does not kill germs*—it merely stops them multiplying. If salmonellae are present in a bird when it goes into a deep-freeze, they are still there and alive when it comes out. Now it takes up to 12 hours to thoroughly thaw a big bird. If the time is greatly cut down, the centre of the bird may still be frozen when cooking begins, and as a result the temperature in the centre may never be high enough to kill salmonellae, even though the outside of the bird is beautifully browned. This is especially liable to occur in spit rotisseries and chicken barbecues, for three reasons: (1) that there is often limited space, and therefore it is difficult to lay out a lot of frozen birds to thaw, (2) that the owner may be in a hurry to get the birds ready for sale, and (3) that in spit roasting, with repeated opening and closing of the doors, the temperature is never high enough to penetrate the deepest part of the carcass. Outbreaks of food poisoning have been caused in this manner (p. 193), and they are becoming commoner.

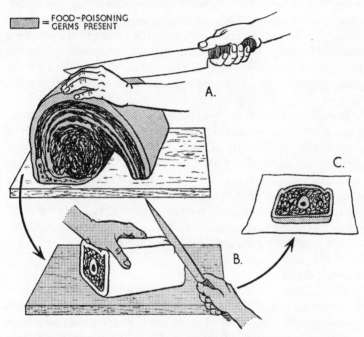

Fig. 8. Germs can spread from raw meat: (*a*) to cooked food, (*b*) they multiply on the latter, (*c*) and give the customer food poisoning

A second danger with cooked poultry is that it may become contaminated after cooking, in the same way as cooked-meat products, by chopping and preparing the cooked bird on the same blocks as the raw birds. In one restaurant outbreak, chickens were cut into portions on a chopping block and cooked thoroughly by boiling. Unfortunately the boiled chickens were prepared for table on the same block, and the diners in the restaurant got food poisoning. Oddly enough the germ was called *Salmonella blockley*.

Butchers' shops

In a butcher's shop, if germs are present on one piece of raw meat, they may easily be spread to other pieces. They can be carried on the butcher's hands; or the counters, the chopping-blocks, the knives and the scales or anything else in the shop, including the refrigerator, may be contaminated and so spread the germs. However, with the exception of sausages (p. 57), the meat will be contaminated only on the surface, and cooking will destroy the germs.

Butchers often sell cooked meats as well as raw; this includes tongue or corned meat sold loose in the shop, pies and all kinds of brawns and jellied meats. If these are touched by hands that have handled raw meat, cut with the same knives, weighed on the same scales, stored in the same refrigerator, or displayed for sale on the same counter, any germs present on the raw meat or on the equipment will be transferred to the food and will multiply on it till eaten by unsuspecting customers. Once again the rule applies— *raw and cooked meat should not be handled together*.

Canning factories

Most canning processes produce a sterile food inside: any bacteria present are killed. Canned food is therefore very safe food indeed, possibly the safest of all. A can is a very sturdy metal box which can take a good deal of buffeting. Very rarely a minute fault develops in a can, and then a drop of water may be sucked inside, and the drop of water may contain dangerous germs. The meat or other food in the can provides ideal conditions for multiplication and when the can is eventually opened, though the food still appears sound, it is teeming with germs. This is nearly always the story when canned food causes disease—accidental contamination of the food through a minute leak in the can after sterilization (p. 197)—but it must be emphasized that such incidents are rare. It has been calculated that there is less than one outbreak of food poisoning for every 400 million cans of food consumed. The risk is very small, but when such an outbreak occurs, it can be devastating (p. 197).

All the above applies to canning methods which aim at sterilization by subjecting the food to very high temperatures. Sometimes this high temperature method is thought to make the meat less attractive, and manufacturers aim only at 'pasteurizing' the meat. This means that not all germs are killed, though most disease germs are. The temperature in the middle of a large can may be very little, if at all, above the temperature needed to kill food-poisoning germs so that the safety margin is small. This method is used mainly for large tins of pork, veal and tongue and these meats are first treated with preserving salts such as nitrates, nitrites and sodium chloride. This pickling followed by pasteurization achieves a fairly high degree of safety: but it is not sterilization, and food-poisoning germs can survive the process (p. 172). It is a method which Health Authorities are watching with some concern.

In this chapter we have followed the trail of infection from the abattoir or poultry plant to the hands of the final customer. Usually this trail ends with the customer receiving a wholesome article of food, but there are hazards on the way, and food hygiene consists in knowing about and facing those hazards.

8

The End of the Trail

Bakehouse, Kitchen and the Home

The trail is long. An ocean voyage in a sack of feeding stuffs, the passage through an animal's intestinal tract and the spread from one animal to another; the journey from farm to farm, then on to market or abattoir, and from there at last to the bakery, kitchen and the home—this is a trail that may take years to cover, but salmonellae are great wanderers and well fitted to stand the buffetings on the way. To some extent they are helped along by man's clumsiness, carelessness or ignorance, but it is only at the end of the food-poisoning trail that these factors become a major menace. This is the menace we must now consider.

A germ looks at a kitchen

For a germ looking for a place to settle down in, a bakehouse or kitchen has many attractions. Apart from one or two very hot spots which must be avoided, the place is pleasantly warm. There are one or two very dry areas, but mostly it is a moist warmth that pervades the atmosphere. Many surfaces are hard and metallic and give no lodgement for ease-loving organisms, but there is usually some softer wooden table, bench or ledge with hair-breadth chinks and cracks into which a wandering germ can retire and raise a family. The air of a kitchen tends to be a little dusty, but the dust contains many nice food particles, and some eventually fall into the chosen chinks and cracks and ensure a food supply for the resident germs. A food-poisoning germ in such a situation has a long and fruitful life ahead of it.

Entry of germs

How do food-poisoning germs get into the bakehouse and kitchen? As far as salmonellae are concerned, we have seen that they may already be present on the surface of raw meat or inside raw sausages. They may also be introduced by a member of the kitchen staff who happens to be a salmonella carrier. Such a person has probably had an attack of diarrhoea some time in the past, and, though now perfectly fit, continues to pass the germ in his faeces. It is all too easy to contaminate the hands at toilet and salmonellae may thereby get on the fingers and be transferred in the kitchen to food or cooking equipment (p. 206). Workers in kitchens and bakehouses may be infected by the contaminated food that is passing through their hands, and it is not uncommon, in an outbreak of food-poisoning, to find that several of the employees are excreting the germ in their faeces (p. 206).

The germs of dysentery, the shigellae, are parasites of man only, so that if a food-borne outbreak of dysentery occurs there must be a human carrier among the kitchen staff. He or she has probably had an attack of diarrhoea a short time ago, and it is usually easy to find the germ by examining a specimen of faeces in the laboratory.

Clostridum welchii is a common germ (p. 36). It is present in dust and soil, and may easily find its way into kitchens and bakehouses, on boots or packing cases, or on sacks of potatoes or vegetables. It is often present in the intestines of man and animals, so that it may find its way on to raw meat or the fingers of people handling it. In a contaminated kitchen it may be present almost anywhere, so that if an outbreak of *Clostridium welchii* food poisoning occurs, it is almost impossible to pin down the source of entry of the germ. Fortunately it is rather fussy about the conditions in which it multiplies (p. 37).

Staphylococci are among the commonest of germs and some staphylococci can be found on the skin of nearly everyone. Fortunately most of these are non-pathogenic (p. 33) and cannot cause disease, but some are pathogenic, though most of these are still not of the food-poisoning variety (p. 34). The commonest

65

sites are the nose and the hands. Often there are no signs at all on the nose or hands of the carrier, and the staphylococci are found only when swabs are taken to the laboratory. Sometimes the infected worker has a sore on the fingers or on the nostrils—a small septic spot or boil is the commonest finding. When this is so, he or she can shed millions of germs into the surroundings and into the food he or she is preparing.

Bacillus cereus is a common germ. It can be found in dust, soil and on green vegetables and potatoes. It is easily destroyed by proper cooking, but if it finds its way into tepid rice and is allowed to multiply in it all night in a warm room it can cause food poisoning even after gentle frying next day (p. 42).

Germs all over the place

When germs get into a place where food is prepared they can spread in an astonishing manner, and it is quite easy to grow them from tables, floors, window-ledges, taps, bowls, dish-cloth, napkins and brushes, as well as from food utensils. It is not easy to keep them out, but one rule which follows from what has been said above is: *Workers who have any skin sores or have recently had diarrhoea must not be allowed to work where food is being prepared.*

The Manipulation of Food

Germs don't jump into food. They have got to be placed there. This involves manipulation or handling of food. Manipulation comes from the Latin word, *manus*, the hand, so it means the same as handling, i.e. touching or moving food by hand. The chef or baker can contaminate food directly with the germs from his own hands, by handling the food on some contaminated surface or in some contaminated bowl or basin, or by placing it against some previously contaminated food. The raw materials are present in abundance—meat, lard, eggs, flour—and germs can easily be added to them. When the two come together, the raw materials and the germs, how do the involved manipulations of cooking affect the outcome?

66

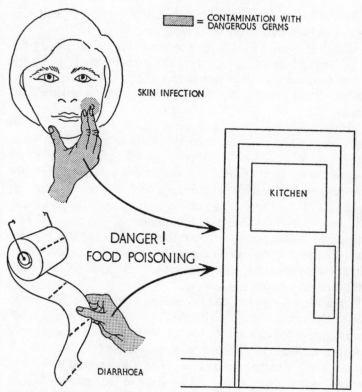

= CONTAMINATION WITH DANGEROUS GERMS

SKIN INFECTION

KITCHEN

DANGER !
FOOD POISONING

DIARRHOEA

FIG. 9. Workers with skin sores or bowel upset must not handle food

Roasting, boiling, frying, stewing

When fresh food is roasted, boiled, fried or stewed for adequate periods, the cooked food is always safe to eat. *Food poisoning cannot be caused by fresh, fully-cooked food eaten hot from the stove.* The important words are 'fresh', 'fully-cooked' and 'eaten hot'. If any of the three are left out the guarantee of safety no longer holds. If the food is deep-frozen, inadequate thawing may prevent heat penetration (p. 60); if the food is only lightly cooked, the temperature may not rise high enough to kill pathogenic germs; if the food is allowed to cool for hours before being eaten, germs may get in and multiply in the tepid food.

Safety in cooked food is the product of temperature and time. The temperature which matters is the temperature in the centre. Most foodstuffs are poor conductors of heat. This means that it takes a long time for the heat on the outside to penetrate the inside.

For a pie or joint of 6 lb. weight a gas-oven mark 4 to 6 might be chosen. This corresponds to an oven temperature of 176° C. to 204° C. (350° F. to 400° F.). This is the temperature applied to the outside of the joint or pie, but it would take at least 2½ hours for the temperature in the centre to reach 100° C. (212° F. or boiling-point). The common cooking rule of 20 minutes to the pound and 20 over is barely sufficient, but 30 minutes to the pound is adequate. Of course, food-poisoning germs are killed at temperatures well below boiling-point (Chapter 2), and in any case these organisms cannot be present inside a fresh, solid joint, though there might be some inside a pie.

Underdone or rare? Rolled joints are a different problem, for in these the outside of the meat is rolled into the inside and food-poisoning germs can be rolled in too: but if time and temperature are correct, they are all killed. Many people like their roast beef or steaks rare or underdone. The colour of cooking meat turns from red to brown at about 70° C. (158° F.), and red beef may be well below this, perhaps just a little over 60° C. (140° F.). It takes up to ½ hour at 60° C. to kill food-poisoning germs, so there is not much margin. *Chacun à son goût.*

Light cooking

Cooking may be 'light' because of low temperature, short time, or both. Cooking fat melts and reaches a temperature of 149° C. (300° F.) before it begins to smoke and burns. If sausages are cooked in such fat, left in long enough and turned till brown on both sides, any salmonellae in the centre are killed. If they are fried at a lower temperature or for too short a time, the temperature in the centre will not be high enough, and we have already

68

seen that salmonellae may survive gentle frying inside a sausage for 15 minutes (p. 58). A steak well fried is sterile, but if the centre is rare it may not be: the temperature of the rare bit may be just marginally above 60° C. (140° F.) and if the time is less than 30 minutes, salmonellae could survive the ordeal. A hard fried egg is safe, for the egg coagulates at 72° C. (161° F.), well above the lethal point for food-poisoning germs: but a soft fried egg could still contain live salmonellae. With hen eggs this is most unlikely, for though salmonellae can be present in the shell they are not present inside: but duck eggs may have salmonellae inside them. The danger from hen eggs arises mainly from bulk liquid or dried egg, not from shell eggs (p. 102).

Most people like an omelette to be moist in the centre. This means that the egg albumen has not coagulated so that the temperature is below 72° C. (161° F.): as the cooking time is very short, food-poisoning germs could escape. This might be a danger with omelettes made from duck eggs. Baked egg custard is usually cooked at oven gas mark 4 or 176° C. (350° F.) for about ½ hour: if the custard sets properly, the internal temperature must be at least 72° C. (161° F.) and any salmonella present will be killed: but if the custard is only half cooked, germs could survive, and outbreaks of food poisoning have been caused in this way (p. 102). In pouring custard, the temperature must be kept below boiling after the eggs have been added to the milk and as the cooking time is short, food-poisoning germs might survive. However if the custards are made from freshly-broken shell hen eggs there is no danger, for salmonellae on the shells, if they got into the eggs while being broken, would not have a chance to multiply. If the eggs are beaten and kept some time before cooking, or if unpasteurized bulk liquid or dried egg is used, the danger is much greater.

Junket is made from warm milk curdled by the action of rennin. The temperature must be kept carefully around body temperature, 37° C. (98° F.), because above that temperature the rennin is destroyed and will not act on the milk. This temperature is ideal for germ multiplication, but if pasteurized milk is used (and no other *should* be used) there is no danger at all, and junket is a thoroughly wholesome food. Sometimes eggs are added to junket: when this is done, germs could be introduced and would thrive rather than be killed at the temperature and time of junket making.

The most dangerous form of light cooking is where the heat is adequate but time too short and this is especially the case with the roasting of chicken and other birds. The difference between a solid lump of fresh meat and a bird is that food-poisoning germs are present only on the surface of the meat, whereas there is every chance that they are present deep in the carcass of a bird. They get there during evisceration if salmonellae are present in the bird's intestine, or the carcass may be contaminated in its journey through the poultry plant (p. 56). It is therefore essential that heat penetrates to the centre of the bird during cooking. It is recommended in some cookery books that $\frac{1}{2}$ to 1 hour's roasting at gas mark 4, 176° C. (350° F.), is sufficient. This may produce nice browning of the outside, but it will not sterilize the inside of the chicken. At least 2 hours at this temperature is necessary for a chicken and much longer is required for big birds. It is most important with deep-frozen birds that they are thoroughly thawed before cooking, otherwise the heat in the centre will be far below sterilizing temperature, and serious outbreaks of food poisoning have occurred in this way (p. 193).

Slow cooling

We have already noted that most foods are poor conductors of heat. They take in heat slowly, but they also give it off slowly. A joint of roast beef, left at room temperature, takes several hours to cool down in the centre, and this applies to pies, tarts, custards and all other cooked foods. At first the temperature falls quickly. (If food is left for only a few minutes before being brought to the table we complain that it is 'cold'.) Later the loss is much slower as the temperature gradient between the food and the surroundings becomes less, and from 50° C. to 37° C. (122° F. to 98·6° F.) it is very slow indeed. Now this is just the temperature range which food-poisoning germs like. Salmonellae revel in such an environment, as do staphylococci and *Clostridium welchii*, and these last two also produce their toxins in food in this temperature range. If a few germs in the food have survived the cooking or if there are germs in the atmosphere of the kitchen, on tables or utensils, in floating dust, or on the hands of food handlers and these germs get into the cooling food, they find conditions ideal and start to

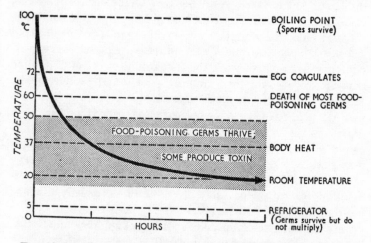

FIG. 10. Food temperature graph. Hot food cools quickly at first then very slowly through the range that suits food-poisoning germs: this is a danger area (p. 68). On the other hand *surface* germs are killed at cooking temperatures

multiply at an alarming rate. A bacteriologist, with all his laboratory know-how, cannot produce a medium that germs like so much as a pie, or a joint or a custard trifle, cooling slowly in a warm kitchen. Remember a germ divides in 20 minutes in good conditions. During a night in a pie, one germ can multiply to several millions.

Staphylococci and *Clostridium welchii* both produce toxin as they multiply, and these toxins, especially staphylococcal toxin, may not be destroyed by boiling (p. 35). Staphylococci grow readily in almost any kind of food, but they like especially meat, trifles, custards, cakes, pies, or cold potatoes. Often this kind of

71

food is allowed to cool slowly, and this is what staphylococci enjoy. They multiply recklessly and produce lots of toxin. The food is probably eaten cold next day, and is bound to cause trouble: but even if it is re-heated, the toxin will not be destroyed.

Clostridium welchii is more fastidious than staphylococci. It dislikes air and oxygen and will not grow on the surface of a cream cake or trifle: it prefers the condition of low oxygen tension which it finds inside a stew or pie. Even very thorough cooking does not kill clostridial spores, and if a few of these are present in a slowly cooling stew or pie, they germinate at around 50° C. (122° F.) and the vegetative germs then multiply quickly and produce toxin. Ideal conditions are provided when a stew is kept warm in a bain-marie (Fig. 2, p. 24), or when cooked meat is sliced, covered with gravy and kept warm on a hot plate. Such food after a few hours can be teeming with germs and also full of toxin, and the two together cause food poisoning. Often this food is eaten the same day without further heating, but even if the food is left to cool overnight and served the next day, the re-heating is usually anything but thorough, and both germs and toxin survive. If meat, or stew or pies are not eaten immediately after cooking, they must either be kept at a temperature well above 60° C. (140° F.) till served, or cooled very quickly and kept in a refrigerator till required for re-heating. The re-heating next day should be thorough, but in large establishments it is much safer to have a rule that all food is eaten the day it is cooked. *Slow cooling of hot food is more dangerous than any other kitchen procedure.*

Left-overs

If the advice just given above is followed, there can, of course, be no left-overs. When there are, they are dangerous, unless great care is taken. First of all, the use of left-overs involves the handling of cold cooked food, for example in the making of rissoles, patties, shepherd's pie and the like. It is easy during such handling for germs to enter the food, either from some contaminated surface or utensil, or from the fingers of the cook who handles the food. Often the rissoles are prepared in the evening from left-overs of the day's food, and not re-cooked till the next day. If the rissoles or patties are left in a warm pantry overnight, the germs inside have plenty of time to multiply. Next morning, they may be fried for breakfast, but the frying amounts to little more than making the outside a nice golden brown. In the centre the temperature is far below the outside temperature, and there is little hope of killing germs and none at all of destroying toxin. If left-overs are used at all, the food should be quickly cooled, and stored in a refrigerator overnight, and not shaped or handled until just before cooking. And the cooking must be thorough, not just gentle warming. Failure to observe these rules can result in an outbreak of food poisoning or dysentery (p. 201).

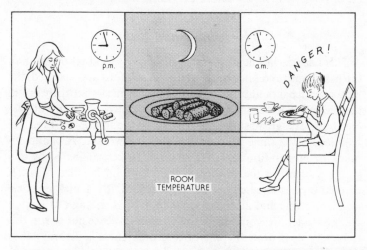

Fig. 11. Left-overs can be dangerous. If used at all they should be stored overnight in a refrigerator and cooked thoroughly next morning

Cold buffet

There are few sights more attractive to the eye of a hungry man (or woman) than an elaborate cold buffet. Golden brown chicken cutlets, cold sausages, boiled hams, galantines, potato salads, meat pies, stuffed pastries, creams, cakes, gateaux and trifles—all tantalizingly attractive, but all foods that require a good deal of handling in their preparation. For convenience, the buffet table has often to be laid and furnished several hours before the meal and this means that the food is left for those hours at room temperature—and the room is often very warm. Unless the food has been prepared with scrupulous care, germs may be present in it, and they are given time to multiply in it while the food lies on the buffet table. Many outbreaks of food poisoning have followed cold buffet meals (p. 202). The safeguards are obvious from what has been said above: the food must be quickly cooled after cooking, and stored overnight in a refrigerator, and kept there till the latest possible moment before the buffet meal.

Keeping Food Safe

This chapter has dealt with the hazards of food preparation in the bakehouse and kitchen. If all the precautions are observed, the final product should be wholesome and harmless, but there is still the danger that the food can be contaminated *after* careful preparation. The greatest danger is when raw and cooked food are handled in the same area or by the same worker. A chopping-block or preparation table is certain to be contaminated by any germs present on the surface of the raw food handled on it. If cooked food is handled on the same surface, it will pick up some of those germs and all the care taken in the cooking of the food will be wasted. It would seem to be common sense not to run this risk, yet this is probably one of the commonest faults in kitchen routine, and food poisoning has been caused in this way (p. 62). Any utensil or container, a knife or a jug for example, used for raw food is contaminated by it. It is madness to use them for cooked food, but this happens commonly.

It is all so easy to appreciate these facts in theory, but it is not so easy to realize them when at work in a clean kitchen. The important word in that sentence is 'clean'. 'Clean' does not mean the same as 'safe', for germs are invisible: one cannot see them on a clean knife, a clean jug, or a clean slicing machine. One cannot see them on a clean table or in the clean air of the kitchen, but if one remembers that invisible germs may be present on raw food and are only too ready to spread to cooked food, one can take steps to make this difficult for them. *Cooked food should never be handled in the same area as raw food: utensils used for raw food must be sterilized before being used for cooked food.*

The reader may feel at the end of this chapter that no food that has passed through a kitchen is fit for human consumption. A sense of proportion is needed. Many millions of people eat many tons of food prepared in many thousands of kitchens every day without coming to harm. Sometimes something goes wrong. Food hygiene consists in trying to prevent this.

9

Other Forms of Food Poisoning

So far in this book we have thought of food poisoning as being caused by germs that live and multiply in our food, and this is certainly the commonest form of food poisoning today, and the one against which the food hygienist must be constantly battling. Other forms of food poisoning are caused by chemicals or impurities getting into sound food, or when we eat, by mistake, substances which are poisonous but resemble edible foods. The commonest of the former type is metallic poisoning, and of the latter type the best known is mushroom poisoning. One or two of these will now be briefly discussed.

Metallic or chemical poisoning

This may occur when metal from a pan or container seeps into the food it contains. Usually the food is acid and the pan made either of galvanized iron or cheap enamel that has become chipped. Outbreaks of zinc poisoning have occurred when stewed apples or other acid fruits have been prepared in galvanized iron pans. The commonest symptom is severe vomiting and this may occur within minutes, or after an hour or two, depending on the concentration of zinc in the food. In one outbreak, alcoholic punch was stored in galvanized containers for over 50 hours and contained zinc in a concentration of 2,200 parts per million: many of those who drank it were vomiting within 20 minutes and nearly all the guests were ill within the hour. Sometimes severe diarrhoea is the most prominent symptom, as in one outbreak caused by a meal of chicken and spinach which had been stored in a galvanized tub after preparation. In another outbreak, fortunately not serious, iced lollies were the cause of zinc poisoning, and in the past, antimony poisoning was sometimes caused by storing lemonade and other acid drinks in chipped enamel jugs.

Metallic poisoning has never been reported from the use of aluminium, iron, tin or stainless steel pans or containers, and zinc poisoning from galvanized pans is now very rare, for the danger is well known. When metallic or other chemical poisoning occurs nowadays it usually follows some accidental contamination. In one outbreak potassium bromate got into sugar used in cakes, and, in another, barium carbonate was used instead of potato starch in a sausage mix. Copper poisoning has been caused by making coffee with water from a dilapidated electric boiler. However, all these forms of chemical or metallic poisoning are rare indeed, and provided food is prepared and stored in sound equipment the danger of such poisoning can be almost disregarded.

Unusual and sometimes very serious forms of poisoning have resulted when food being carried in a van or a ship has been accidently contaminated with a chemical that has leaked from another part of the cargo. Four serious outbreaks of food poisoning were caused in this way in Saudi Arabia in 1966. Flour had been shipped from America to Arabia in two ships, and in the same holds, above the flour, was a cargo of liquid endrin, a poisonous insecticide. Some of the liquid leaked and soiled the bags of flour, and when this was made into bread, 874 patients were admitted to hospital with a severe form of food poisoning and 26 patients died in coma. International regulations have since been drafted to prevent such errors in the loading of ships, but tragic mistakes may still be made as unforeseen dangers are revealed. In one outbreak nearer home, in Epping in 1966, 84 patients suffered from jaundice after eating wholemeal bread. The flour had been carried in a van in which there were also jars of a chemical used as a hardener of resin. The liquid had spilled and though there were only traces of it in the flour, this was enough to cause a serious epidemic.

Mushroom poisoning

This name is unfortunate, for there is no such thing as poisoning due to mushrooms. Mushrooms are delicious and wholesome food, as are in fact most fungi found in our woods and meadows, even those we call toadstools; but there are several fungi which contain deadly poisons. Such are the 'fly agaric', *Amanita muscaria*, the 'false blusher', *Amanita pantherina*, the 'death cap', *Amanita phalloides* and the 'destroying angel', *Amanita virosa*. Muscarine and amanitine are two of the poisons concerned and they cause severe vomiting and diarrhoea and often coma and death. Such fungus poisoning is, however, uncommon, for these deadly fungi can be distinguished easily from the edible mushroom. The fly agaric, for example, is bright scarlet with white spots; the 'death cap' is greenish with white gills; the 'false blusher' brown with white spots; the 'destroying angel' is white all over, even its gills; whereas the gills of the edible mushrooms are either pink or brownish-black. The skin of the cap can be peeled easily from the edible mushroom, but this peeling test is a very unsafe one, for some of the poisonous fungi peel easily too. The only safe way, if one wants to be adventurous in eating fungi, is to learn most carefully the distinctive features of the really dangerous ones—there are less than a dozen. Most other fungi can be eaten: a few may cause slight gastro-intestinal upset, without being dangerous, but most are safe and delicious.

Mussel poisoning

While all these forms of poisoning are caused, at least in part, by man's carelessness or ignorance, nature itself can sometimes lay poisonous baits for man. Mussels are normally a delightful food, to those who like them. They feed by straining huge volumes of sea-water through their bodies and sifting out the microscopic specks of animal and plant life in it. Sometimes a population explosion occurs in this microscopic world, and vast multitudes of organisms called dinoflagellates spread over the surface of the sea forming a red fluorescent film. These dinoflagellates produce a poison which does not harm the mussels, but can cause a severe illness in man if he eats them. There was a serious outbreak of this form of poisoning in North-East England in the summer of 1968.

At least 78 people were severely affected with peculiar nervous symptoms, including paralysis; but fortunately none died. There was, however, a great number of deaths among shags and other sea birds that fed on sand eels that were also poisoned by the dinoflagellates, and many starfish that fed on mussels were found dead on the shore.

There is little the food hygienist can do to prevent this form of poisoning. Probably one must look to the biologists and naturalists instead, who could test mussels as the summer advances for the presence of toxin; and dead birds on the sea shore might also give a warning; but these dinoflagellate explosions are rare occurrences, freaks of nature, and one can normally eat one's mussels without fearing any consequences.

Ptomaine poisoning

This term is mentioned because the name still creeps into accounts of food poisoning, especially in the lay press. There is really no such thing. Ptomaines are substances formed in putrefying organic matter such as putrid food. But ptomaines are not poisonous and, in any case, no one eats food so putrid. Food which results in food poisoning is usually fresh and attractive. It is the invisible germs, toxins or chemicals that cause the poisoning. The food itself has not 'gone off' or become tainted. 'Sweet tastes have sour closes.'

10

Other Diseases Spread by Food

Any germ that can survive in food can be conveyed to man by food. It is merely convention that labels only certain food-borne illnesses as food poisoning. Some of the other diseases conveyed by food are much more serious than food poisoning.

Typhoid fever

This disease is caused by a salmonella called *Salmonella typhi* but the disease is very different from salmonella food poisoning. This is because the typhoid salmonella does not stay in the bowel like most other salmonellae, but enters the blood-stream whence it can penetrate almost any organ of the body. The patient suffers a severe prostrating illness with prolonged fever, and there are many dangerous complications. Fortunately an antibiotic called chloramphenicol has a dramatic effect on this disease. If given early, it can bring the illness to an end in a few days and the patient regains his sense of well-being in a week or ten days, instead of suffering a long, muttering, feverish illness for weeks on end.

Typhoid fever is always caught through food or water. The dose of germs may be quite small. Other salmonellae must multiply to great numbers in food before they cause food poisoning, but a few typhoid salmonellae can cause typhoid fever. This is why typhoid fever can be conveyed by water. Germs do not readily multiply in cold water though they can survive in it for weeks on end. Big outbreaks of typhoid fever have been caused through drinking water (p. 214), but there has rarely been a water-borne outbreak of salmonella food poisoning.

Salmonella typhi differs from most other salmonella in another way. It is a parasite of man only. Other salmonellae may be found in creatures as diverse as foxes, pythons, turtles, pigeons and many others as well as man. Not so *Salmonella typhi*; it infects only man. This means, of course, that every case and every outbreak of typhoid fever must originate from typhoid germs passed from another human being. This usually means a typhoid carrier—a man or woman who has recovered from typhoid fever but still passes the germ in his or her faeces or urine. Some carriers continue to do so for many years, even for life. Somehow the germs must find their way into water or food, and this water or food must be swallowed by someone else.

There are often alarming reports about cases of typhoid fever in the press and on radio and television, but typhoid fever does not pass through the air from person to person like measles or influenza. Unless the germs are present in the food or water supply, typhoid fever will not spread, and unless a person swallows water or food with typhoid germs in it, he will not get typhoid fever. The germs get into food usually directly because the carrier is a cook or a food handler. The way they get into water supplies may be much more involved and the unravelling of an outbreak can involve an intricate piece of detective work. Examples of food and water-borne typhoid fever outbreaks are given in Chapter 24 (pp. 198 and 212).

Infectious hepatitis

Infectious hepatitis is jaundice. *Hepar* is the Greek for liver and hepatitis means inflammation of the liver. When the liver is inflamed, bile cannot flow through it so that it gets dammed back into the blood-stream: from there it gets caught in the cells of the skin and conjunctiva, and turns the patient yellow.

The disease is caused by a virus but no one has yet been able to grow this virus. This makes it difficult to be sure of how the disease spreads. It seems to spread from person to person in families and classrooms, and it can also spread from house to house, as if carried by travellers over hill and dale. Usually one case is separated from the next by a month, so that the disease seems to have a long incubation period. Sometimes, however, explosive outbreaks occur and a lot of people go down with jaundice within a short time. This can only mean a common source of infection. In Delhi in 1955 over 29,000 people were affected within 6 weeks and there is no doubt that the outbreak was due to massive contamination of the drinking-water supply. In another very small outbreak, doctors and nurses who had orange juice for breakfast developed jaundice: the orange juice was prepared by a kitchen worker whose husband also had jaundice. In another outbreak in an officers' mess a potato salad seemed to have carried the virus: it had been prepared by a kitchen hand who had himself recently been ill. The eating of shellfish, especially clams, has often been connected with outbreaks in America. In Scandinavia an outbreak of infectious hepatitis was traced to the eating of oysters, and the supplier of the oysters was sued for damages. It seems that food and water play an important part in the spread of this form of jaundice, but just how important it is difficult to judge as we have still no way of getting the virus to grow in the laboratory.

Scarlet fever and diphtheria

Scarlet fever is not a very common disease in Britain today, though in the past there have been big and serious outbreaks. Sometimes these have been conveyed by milk. This may occur in one of two ways. A milker or other dairy worker may be suffering from mild scarlet fever or tonsillitis or be a carrier of the germ called haemolytic streptococcus which causes both these conditions, and germs from his throat, nose or saliva may get into the milk. This is not a very likely method of spread for these germs do not readily multiply in milk at room temperature. A more likely source of a milk-borne outbreak of scarlet fever is inflammation of the udder, or mastitis, in the cow. This is a fairly common condition in cows: it is not usually caused by the scarlet fever streptococcus, but it can be. The germs multiply in the inflamed udder and when the milk is passed it is teeming with them. This has been the usual story in milk-borne outbreaks, but pasteurization kills streptococci, and outbreaks of scarlet fever cannot be caused by pasteurized milk.

Diphtheria is a disease normally spread from one person to another, for the germ is present in the throat and nose of a patient with diphtheria or of a diphtheria carrier. There have in the past been one or two outbreaks conveyed by milk. The milker has usually been a carrier, the diphtheria germ has been conveyed on the hands of the milker to the teats of a cow, a diphtheritic sore has developed on the teats and the germs have passed into the milk. The milkman has then carried the germ in the unpasteurized milk to the customers on his rounds. Pasteurization has abolished this risk, but it was never a serious one: a milk-borne outbreak of diphtheria was an epidemiological curiosity even before the days of pasteurization.

Brucellosis

The germ of this disease is called brucella, named after Dr. Bruce who first discovered it when investigating outbreaks of the disease in Malta. The two commonest strains are *Brucella abortus* and *Brucella melitensis*. The former causes a disease in cattle which often ends in abortion. It is quite common in Britain. The latter causes a wasting disease in goats and sheep, mainly in Mediterranean countries. The infection is conveyed to man either by drinking the milk of cows, goats or ewes or by direct contact with the animals, especially during calving, kidding and lambing. It is a common infection in veterinarians in Britain and also in goat-herdsmen and shepherds in Mediterranean areas.

The disease consists of a long feverish illness with drenching sweats and pains in the bones and joints. Sometimes the fever comes in bouts or waves and the illness is then known as undulant fever. *Brucella melitensis* causes a more severe illness than *Brucella abortus*. It was till recently very common in Malta and was known as Malta fever. The peasants there used to lead their goats into the towns of Floriana and Valetta and milk them at the customers' doors, a very direct producer to consumer service but one which was full of danger to both. Pasteurization is now compulsory in

83

Malta and the disease has almost disappeared, though cases still occur among the peasants who live close to their goats and probably still drink milk raw. In Britain the disease is caused by *Brucella abortus* and infection is derived from cows only. Cases still occur in areas where unpasteurized milk is drunk but it is commonest in veterinarians and farmers who come in close contact with the infected cattle and with the milk before it is pasteurized.

Pasteurization, of course, can only kill the germ after it has passed through and caused illness in the animals. The only final solution to the problem of brucellosis is to carry out tests for brucellosis on all the animals in herds, slaughter those that are positive, and so raise disease-free herds. This would be a formidable task with herds of sheep and goats in the Mediterranean countries, but it is far from impossible with cattle in Britain. It has been done in many European countries and there is now a campaign to deal with the infection in this country too. After all, this was the policy carried out when the problem of tuberculosis in cattle was tackled. Our orthopaedic hospitals used to be full of children suffering from tuberculosis of the bones, joints and spine, all caused from drinking the germs of tuberculosis in milk. We now have tuberculosis-free herds. It is time to get rid of brucellosis too.

The diseases mentioned in this chapter are all food or waterborne. With some of them there is little the food hygienist can do in a direct sense. Brucellosis, for example, does not spread through any fault of the food handler. Typhoid fever, on the other hand, may do so if the food handler is a carrier, or if there are faults in the hygiene of a food-canning factory. It may be spread through a crack in a water main or by the wrong siting of a shallow well (p. 214). Such faults may appear to have little to do with the food hygienist but he has a responsibility to educate others. This he can only do if he himself is aware of the facts.

11

The Water We Drink and the Air We Breathe

All food contains water. The preparation, manipulation and cooking of food involves its use. We even drink water. What *is* this substance, whence comes it, and how does it reach us? Is it safe to use?

Shallow wells and deep wells

The source of our water-supply is rain, which falls from the clouds and soaks into the soil. Were there nothing to stop it, it would sink deeper and deeper and form a vast subterranean ocean of water which we would be able to tap only by enormous bore-holes and wells, but the water is stopped by the rocks under the soil. Sometimes the first layer of rock beneath the top soil is watertight or impermeable, and the rain can sink no further. It therefore collects on top of the rock as sub-soil water, and as the layer of rock is seldom horizontal, this sub-soil water flows under the surface of the earth according to the tilt of the rock. Eventually it forms a basin of water which somewhere, often at the foot of a hill or mountain, breaks surface and gushes out as a spring. We tend to think of a spring as something tiny and secluded, but all streams and rivers have their sources in springs, which must then be enormous. A spring is the natural way by which rain comes to the surface, but man can also reach the sub-soil water by sinking a well and drawing the water up. Such a well may be very deep or quite shallow. It depends how far below the surface is the impermeable first layer of rock, but whether it is deep or shallow, a well which taps the sub-soil water is always known as a *shallow well*.

Sometimes the first layer of rock is permeable; the water then sinks through the rock, perhaps through two or three layers of rock, till it is stopped by a deeper impermeable layer. Man can sink a well by boring down through these layers to tap this supply of water. Such a well is known as a *deep well* because it is sunk through rock. It may or may not be really deep. That depends on the depth of the first impermeable layer, and a deep well in one part of the country might be shallower than a *shallow well* in another. Note the difference between the impermeable first layer and the first impermeable layer.

There are two much more important differences than depth. Water is a powerful solvent, and as it sinks through rock, it may dissolve out some of its substance. If the rock is limestone, the water dissolves some of its calcium, and calcium makes water hard. Deep-well water is therefore often hard, while shallow-well water is soft, for it has not passed through rock. The second point is that a rock, even if it lets water seep through, also acts as a filter, and many impurities, including germs, are filtered out of the water as it sinks through the rock. Deep-well water may therefore be purer than shallow-well water, but the latter is softer.

Rivers, streams and lakes

Rivers and streams, we have seen, are fed by enormous springs. They are really huge masses of water that have escaped from the sub-soil and are moving down an incline to the sea. Lakes are also collections of sub-soil water: some are fed by streams and rivers, while others form on high ground with no visible source of supply: they are simply huge springs. The water in the rivers, streams and lakes, when used as a water supply, is known as upland-surface water.

Is water a safe drink?

As the rain falls through the air it may dissolve traces of impurities, such as sulphur, from our smoky atmosphere, but it is free from germs and safe to drink. Once it starts sinking through the soil, its safety can no longer be guaranteed, for the soil is full of germs that can be washed into the sub-soil water. Most of these germs are harmless to man, but disease germs can get into the sub-soil water too. This can happen, for example, if there is any defect in a drain or sewer which allows sewage to escape into the ground, for this is bound to flow into the sub-soil water and carry any germs with it. Septic tanks and cesspools often leak and may cause

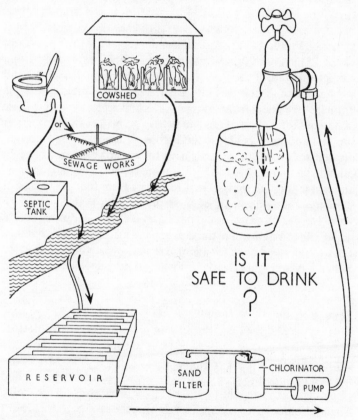

IS IT SAFE TO DRINK ?

FIG. 12. Rivers and lakes are often badly polluted. Water is safe to drink only if all precautions are taken to remove dangerous germs from it before it reaches our taps

87

serious contamination of the sub-soil water with dangerous germs. On farms there are always heaps of animal manure, and liquid drains from this into sub-soil water. Clearly it is important that shallow wells should be so sited that impure water from such sources cannot drain into them. Yet many outbreaks of disease have been caused in this way.

Rivers and streams may obviously be polluted by everything that flows into them. This includes waste products from factories, but also water from countless rivulets, ditches, drains and effluents. Every agricultural field has drains under it and a farmer pays rates to the River Board into whose waters his fields eventually drain. He spreads fertilizers, pesticides and manure on his fields, and seepage can and does get into the rivers. More important is the drainage or effluent from sewage works and septic tanks, for these often contain disease germs, and these germs get into our water supplies and must be destroyed before we use it. If they are not, disaster follows if the water is used for cooling cans of meat in a canning factory (p. 198) or for drinking (p. 80). This talk on wells and water supplies may seem a long way from food hygiene, but there is scarcely any part of food preparation that does not involve the use of water. It cannot harm a chef, a shopkeeper or a housewife to know where the tap-water comes from and what it is. Let us look quickly at sewage works and waterworks so that we can understand more clearly just what comes out when we turn on the tap.

Sewage works

Most people think the purpose of sewage works is to destroy germs. This is not so. Their purpose is to cut down the amount of organic matter flowing into our rivers. This is done first by removing most of the solid matter by screens or coarse filters, and secondly by exposing the liquid part to both aerobic and anaerobic bacterial action. This is done by allowing the sewage to trickle out of rotating sprinklers and sink down through filter beds. (You can often see these working from a train window.) The action of the air and the bacteria is to break down the organic particles into simpler substances. This process requires a lot of oxygen, and the aim of the sewage treatment is to decrease this biochemical oxygen demand (the B.O.D.) of the crude sewage before it goes into the rivers. If the sewage were discharged untreated into rivers, it would use up all the oxygen dissolved in the water, and water plants and fish, bereft of oxygen, would die. Our rivers would be aesthetically more unpleasing than they are now, but the primary purpose of sewage works is to save river oxygen, not to please the eye.

During sewage purification as described above—and septic tanks work on similar principles—some disease germs may die, but many do not. If there are cases of typhoid fever or polio-myelitis in a town, the germs of these diseases will almost certainly be found in the effluent flowing from the town's sewage works where it runs into the river. Carriers of disease germs have been detected by soaking swabs in the effluent and then trying to trace back from there by drain swabs to the water closet of the carrier (p. 214).

Waterworks

Waterworks take their water straight from rivers and lakes. Now disease germs do not find water a very nourishing fluid, and so one of the main purifying methods in a waterworks is simply to hold the water for several weeks in an attempt to starve the germs. A reservoir is not so simple as it looks on the surface. There are long walls or baffles in it and water coming in at one end has a long, tortuous journey before it gets out at the other. It probably takes about three weeks, and in this time a lot of fine suspended particles will settle to the bottom and many germs will die: but not all. Typhoid germs and many viruses can survive these bleak weeks. The water coming from the reservoirs is therefore led through very fine sand filters which remove any particulate matter still in it and also many germs, and, after filtration, it is usually treated with chlorine which kills most of those that survive to this stage. The treated water then goes to the pumping stations and is pumped into our water mains and so into our taps. It is a long process, and obviously a fault anywhere along the line could lead to trouble. Our water engineers are constantly watching and improving the processes: our bacteriologists and our virologists are constantly testing the final product.

This may seem a long diatribe about something rather remote from food poisoning. The thoughtful food hygienist will realise how much he depends on a safe water supply.

Air

If a bacteriologist leaves a plate of culture medium exposed to the air, germs will grow on it. They can only come from the air. A hospital bacteriologist often does this very thing when he is trying to trace the spread of infection in a ward or operating theatre. A public health bacteriologist may do exactly the same when investigating outbreaks of food poisoning traced to a bakery, kitchen or a factory. Air is not germ-free, certainly not the air inside a building. It carries germs breathed out by people when they speak, and especially when they cough or sneeze. It carries germs stirred up from the floor during sweeping, from people's clothes and boots as they walk, and from any powder or dusty material, such as flour or dried egg, that may be used in baking processes. Moulds and yeasts float through the air. If they land on bread or cheese, they will soon cover it with greenery: if they alight on fruit or juices, they start fermenting them, changing the sugar in them into alcohol. If there are disease germs anywhere, on the hands, boots, clothes or hair of a person, or on any food, or other material he is working with, these germs can easily be wafted into the air and spread all over the place. The moral of this for the food hygienist is not to stop breathing, but to see that everything is done to prevent germs getting into the air, and to keep food covered and protected so that if there are any air-borne germs around, at least they cannot come down on the food.

Part 2

12

A Look at the Menu

Hors-d'Oeuvre to the Main Course

Since Eve ate apples, much depends on dinner.

Byron, Don Juan

As the diner reads it

A restaurant menu makes more demands on its readers than any
other form of literature. Its shape is usually awkward, being much
wider and taller than a book of poems, a play or a novel. It is more
akin to a sheet of music, which can be troublesome enough, but
with a menu one is not supplied with a stand.

There is a time limit for reading a menu: it cannot be laid aside
to be taken up later. Although its scope is vast, it must be com-
prehended quickly, often under the eye of a supervisor who knows
its contents by heart. Several people round a table may be given a
copy of the menu, and then they are very like card players studying
their hands. But they are not nearly so confident when making
their calls, and often revoke in a manner that would not be tolerated at bridge. In the worst cases the supervisor has to take over.

So much for the strains and hesitations. Menu reading has its
rewarding side as well, and there is probably no other literary form
which can excite the imagination and the senses so strongly. The
tempting smells, tastes and colours of the dishes are called up, and,
in addition, the imagination paints still-lifes of pantry tables laden
with fish, joints and game, vegetables and fruits, spices, vinegars
and oils, creams, sugars and sponges, as well as pictures of ships
and planes conveying these from the corners of the earth, and
armies of chefs, confectioners and pastrycooks eager to fashion
them into masterpieces of the culinary art.

93

Another point of view

Such is, or ought to be, the effect of the menu on the customer. He should have no reservations about the quality or attractiveness of the dishes it describes. The food hygienist looks at the menu from a different viewpoint; he is concerned with the wholesomeness and safety of the food provided. Let us, as food hygienists, glance through a menu, bearing in mind all that has been discussed in the earlier chapters of this book.

Hors-d'oeuvre

These are snacks, additional to the meal by definition. They titivate the appetite for what comes after and so must be light and delicate. They should catch the diner's eye, and through his eye stimulate his mouth and his stomach. All the cunning of the larder chef is needed to achieve a harmony of colour and design, with his pastry barquettes and allumettes and his canapés of toast, and the multitude of forcemeats and fillings with which he garnishes them. Then there are anchovies and pieces of ham, slices of mortadella and salami, fish, eggs, eels, olives, asparagus, peppers, chervil and parsley. It all makes quite a show, but it involves a good deal of handling behind the scenes. Most of the constituents of a tray of hors-d'oeuvre are very safe foods. Pastry and toast do not encourage bacterial life, and anchovies, herrings, peppers and olives are too salty, too acid or too oily to allow bacteria to multiply. Hams, sausages and fillings carry some risks, for they may be contaminated during handling, and, as they lie on the trolley for several hours during meal service, germs have time to multiply on them before the last diners are fed. These foods must therefore be prepared with scrupulous care, separately from any raw meat, and kept cold till required. Hors-d'oeuvre are really a form of cold buffet, and the same precautions apply (p. 73).

Soups and broths

Soups and broths are boiled slowly for hours, and are sterile when served hot. One can scarcely eat a safer food. Yet a consommé or broth is very little different from the fluid media used in laboratories for coaxing germs to grow. In fact, bacteriologists call their media broth, but they do not use it boiling hot, for that would kill their precious germs. Herein lies the only danger of soups and broths. They should not be allowed to cool slowly and then be left tepid for hours, for if germs get into the pot they will grow rapidly in such an ideal medium. If such a broth is reheated, vegetative germs might be killed but toxins might not be destroyed, and outbreaks of food poisoning have been caused in this way.

Cold consommé is safe only if it has been cooled quickly and kept in a refrigerator, but if there is any carelessness in its preparation, it can become a consommé of germs. Ideally soups and broths should be consumed on the day they are cooked, without any cooling and re-heating. Stock-pots should be looked on with suspicion: if tolerated at all, they should be maintained near boiling-point and kept carefully covered. Otherwise they are dangerous.

Fish

The diner may relax when he comes to this course, for there is little to fear from fish. Food-poisoning germs do not inhabit the intestines of fish, for fish are cold-blooded animals, and salmonellae and clostridia like a bit of warmth in their habitats. In some waters the germs of botulism get into fish, and in fermenting fish dishes the germ may multiply and cause botulism (p. 120). But such dishes are served in tents and wigwams, not in restaurants, and the diner in the latter may order any fish on the menu with complete confidence.

Shellfish in a restaurant is almost certainly safe, for there are regulations covering its gathering and cleansing. Mussels, oysters and cockles are gathered in shallow inshore waters which are often polluted by sewage, and salmonellae may well be present in such waters. Shellfish suck great quantities of water through their bodies, filtering minute food particles from it for their nourishment. Unfortunately they also filter out any germs that are present.

and build up a high concentration in their body tissues. People have bathed in such water without coming to any harm, but have caught typhoid fever from eating shellfish gathered there. Just as shellfish become infected from filtering polluted water so they cleanse themselves when put in tanks of clean water, and this is the basis of purification techniques required by law. If shellfish are on the menu, it can be assumed they conform to the law and have no stains on their character.

When fish is left over and compounded with potatoes into patties or fish cakes, it loses its good name and acquires all the disadvantages of left-over cookery (p. 72). Salmonellae or staphylococci may be added from the hands of food handlers or from any contaminated dust or debris in a sub-standard kitchen. Outbreaks of food poisoning or even dysentery (p. 201) have been caused in this way, but it is the handling, not the fish, that is to blame.

The main course
Meat. The roast beef of Old England can stand up to any safety tests. It is well browned on the outside, and even if the centre is still rare, no germs can get through its tough exterior, provided it is not a rolled rib roast (p. 68). Served hot from the oven it can be offered to friend or foe, Englishman or foreigner, without a thought for any intestinal repercussions. It is staunch and sterile. The same cannot always be said for the gravy. If this is prepared straight from the roasting pan it can be poured with confidence over a plate of roast beef and Yorkshire pudding, and can be a noble addition to the national ensemble. But sometimes gravies come by devious routes from dubious stock-pots and pass through lingering temperatures on the way. Such infusions are not germ proof.

What has been said of roast beef is true of grilled steaks. They are sterile. They may be tough, but, from the bacteriological point of view, they are fit to eat. Stews are not so safe: one wants to know something of their history. If they are cooked on the day they are eaten and served hot from the pot they cannot contain germs; but if the stew has been allowed to cool, or kept just warm for several hours before being brought to the table, anaerobic organisms like *Clostridium welchii* may have got into it and multiplied, and the stew may be full of germs and toxins (p. 192). The same is true of any beef, pork, mutton or ham prepared long before the meal, covered with gravy, and kept warm for hours on a hot plate or in a bain-marie (p. 72).

Ragouts and blanquettes are normally made from fresh meat, veal, chicken or mutton, and if the cooking is thorough and continuous, as it should be, they are wholesome and sterile. If there is any interruption in the cooking, or worse, if they are allowed to cool and are kept for re-heating next day, they can be the most dangerous of meat dishes for, when cool or tepid, they are ideal culture media for anaerobic germs (p. 72). A blanquette is sometimes made from left-over beef or pork: the *velouté* or white sauce is made by mixing white stock with the roux of flour and butter, and sometimes yolks of eggs are added at the last moment to make Allemande sauce. This is poured over the meat, and the total amount of cooking the blanquette gets may be minimal—all very well if the cold meat is sterile to start with, but not enough to kill any germs that may be present in it.

Pies and poultry. A pie is described in the cookery books as a pastry case consisting of a bottom, sides and top, enclosing a filling of meat, mutton, poultry, game or pork. This is a prosaic view of a romantic object. Into a pie may go beef from the Argentine, mutton from Australia, wheat from Canadian prairies, spice from the Orient, lemon juice from the Mediterranean, lard from a Danish piggery and butter from an English dairy farm. The constituents are blended and baked with skill and the finished product is a work of art. It is also unfortunately a potential nest of infection. The geographical background of the pie exposes it to all the bacterial hazards of animal husbandry, transport and slaughter (Chapters 5–7), and even if it escapes these, contamination can occur in the bakehouse or kitchen, and salmonellae, staphylococci or clostridia can be stowed away deep in the heart of the pie. The key to safety lies in heat penetration; a golden crust does not guarantee this (p. 59).

Poultry flocks are often infected with salmonellae, and these germs are present in the centre of the carcass, not as with meat, on the surface only (p. 60). This means that thorough cooking is essential. Roast beef, with a rare centre, is a safe dish for there are no germs in the centre of a joint, unless it is rolled rib roast (p. 68), but an underdone chicken is quite a different matter, for it is the deeper parts of the bird that are liable to be contaminated by germs in its intestines, and if the temperature does not rise high enough in the centre, the germs survive the cooking. A fresh chicken after roasting is likely to be thoroughly cooked, but with a deep-freeze bird, unless thawing is thorough the centre of the bird may be very underdone, and outbreaks of food poisoning have been caused in this way (p. 193).

Game birds are usually free from dangerous germs in the wild state. Contamination may occur from faulty preparation, especially if cooling and re-heating are involved. The centre of a cold game pie is an anaerobic reserve and clostridia can flourish there with little competition.

The cold table. Cold meats are attractive viands both to man and microbes. The latter can share the dish only through faults in preparation. Microbes get their best chance to invade the meat after it has been cooked and while it is still cooling. They must, of course, be helped on to it, for the distances the most mobile germs can cover on their own are entirely microscopic. So the food handler must help the germs along, by transferring them from his own person or from some contaminated raw meat to the cooked food (Chapter 8). Once in the food, and the temperature right, food-poisoning germs get a new zest for life.

Vegetables, pickles and sauces. Vegetables when cooked are very safe foods, and even raw they rarely cause trouble. Salads are often suspect, but the water they are washed in, or the dressing they are smeared with, may be more to blame than the greens, cucumbers or tomatoes. If there is any doubt these can be washed in chlorinated water (p. 31), and this may be advisable when fresh vegetables have to be stored a long time as, for example, on board ship.

Germs do not like acid, so pickles and sauces made with vinegar are likely to be germ free. Aigre-douce sauce has vinegar and wine in it, as has *Lyonnaise* sauce; and bigarade sauce is sharpened with the juice of bitter orange; but bread sauce is compounded of breadcrumbs and butter, with consommé or stock added to it, a slightly risky combination if there are faults in stock-pot hygiene. *Béchamel* is a sauce of milk, flour and butter, safe enough if made and served the same day, but a good medium for germs when tepid. *Hollandaise* sauce is pure butter and yolk of eggs, probably too rich in fat for the easy growth of germs, but if the eggs are contaminated with salmonellae, they might overcome this difficulty and multiply. *Velouté* is a basic white sauce made of white stock mixed with flour and butter: made properly, it is cooked for over an hour and must then be sterile, and if used at once is above all suspicion. It may, however, be strained through a cloth and beaten till cold, both manipulations which may cause contamination. It is then used as a base for many other sauces, and some new ingredient may add to the danger. White sauces in general are good media for germs except when cooked for a meal, and served hot with it. It may be convenient to prepare them in advance and keep them overnight, but it is not sound food hygiene to do so.

Mayonnaise and salad dressing. Mayonnaise is a slightly mysterious substance, both in the origin of its name and sometimes in its preparation. Some hold it should be magnonaise from *manier*, to stir, a likely enough derivation, for stirring is the essence of mayonnaise preparation. Others say it should be mahonnaise from Port Mahon in Minorca, possibly because of the olive oil imported thence to France after the place was taken by the Duc de Richelieu in the mid-eighteenth century. A third view is that it is a corruption of Moyeunaise from the Old French *moyeu*, meaning the yolk of an egg. All three suggestions are plausible, for this sauce is certainly a combination of egg yolk and olive oil which has to be stirred to make it into mayonnaise. The only other constituent is vinegar, and of this there may be much or little. This last ingredient is the most important from the food hygienist's point of view, for if a lot is added, the mayonnaise will be too acid for germs, but if only a teaspoonful or two, they could multiply in the mixture. Made fresh from egg yolks, as it usually is, mayonnaise is a safe food: but if the yolks are separated and kept for some time before being used, salmonellae could grow in them and would not be killed when beaten into mayonnaise, for no cooking is involved. However as far as food poisoning is concerned, the record of mayonnaise is a good one.

Salad dressing is pure oil and vinegar, and food-poisoning germs will not grow in such an oily acid mixture. Salad cream is sometimes made from the sieved yolks of boiled eggs mixed with cream and vinegar without further cooking. This is fine if the cream is safe, but unfortunately this cannot be taken for granted (p. 105). Sometimes flour is added and raw egg yolk, and unless such a mixture is well acidified with vinegar it could furnish food-poisoning germs with a very attractive medium in which to grow.

This takes the customer through the serious part of the restaurant menu. 'Unquiet meals make ill digestions' and our diner may already have dined neither wisely nor well. Whether he suffers any bacterial ill-effects depends on the measure of care taken in the preparation of his meal. Most meals are thoroughly wholesome, most dishes free of any unpleasant germ. To study those that are not, and to understand the reason why, is the point of this chapter and the purpose of this book.

13

A Look at the Menu

Sweets and Cheese

Things sweet to taste prove in digestion sour.
Shakespeare. *Richard II*

The latter part is the lighter part of a meal. A good deal of it is mere froth and air, and a vast amount of beating and whipping goes into the preparation of many of the items that grace this part of the menu. Gateaux and entremets, soufflés and charlottes, sponges and creams are all airy delicacies, but the air they contain is beaten into ingredients that cannot be taken too lightly, for they are heavy in calories. Eggs, milk, cream, butter and sugar form the basis of most of them, with flavourings and colourings added to charm the eye and tantalize the palate.

A full menu lists a wide variety of sweets. There are pastry sweets such as tarts, pies and flans, and the heavier sweets such as rice and semolina and weighty boiled puddings; meringue sweets and whipped cream sweets, ice-creams and fruit sweets; custards and caramels, sweet omelettes, crêpes and fritters; cream cakes or gateaux, trifles, charlottes, sponges, soufflés, moulds, fools and jellies. They are the products of ingenuity and art, but also unfortunately of constituents which must be scrutinized for their liability to convey food poisoning.

Constituents of Sweets

Eggs

We have already seen that poultry may be heavily infected with salmonellae (p. 51), and it is not surprising that eggs become contaminated. If an egg is dry and cold, germs find it difficult to get through the shell: eggs have, for example, been soaked in a liquid culture of salmonellae in the laboratory, but no salmonellae have been found inside the egg. If a warm moist egg is laid on cold wet ground, however, salmonellae may be sucked through as the egg cools, and this may explain why germs are found more often inside duck eggs than hen eggs, for ducks often lay their eggs out in the open, while hens prefer a warm dry nest. The percentage of eggs infected inside the shell is quite low and there is rarely any danger in eating a boiled egg, but salmonellae are very often present on the shells, of hen and duck eggs alike, and when eggs are broken in bulk to form commercial liquid egg, salmonellae from the shells or from the odd infected yolk get into the mix and then multiply and contaminate vast quantities of the product.

Bulk liquid or dried egg has been responsible for many outbreaks of food poisoning, and many foreign salmonellae have crossed the oceans in these products (p. 22). When they are used in bakeries and kitchens, the liquid and powder contaminate utensils and tables, and the egg dust can form an aerosol or mist of infectious particles. Baking with egg depends on its coagulation, and this begins at 72° C. (161·6° F.), well above the death point of salmonellae which is around 60° C. (140° F.). Cakes, sponges, swiss rolls, custard tarts and other egg products are therefore sterile when they come out of the oven, but may easily be contaminated again as they cool on a table in the air of the kitchen or bakehouse. Much more dangerous are the confectionery practices which do not involve cooking the eggs: fillings for cakes and buns often contain artificial cream or raw whipped egg, and these have caused serious outbreaks of food poisoning (p. 205).

Dried egg is produced either by forcing the liquid egg as a spray into a warm chamber where it falls to the floor as a powder, or by spreading it on warm rollers where it forms a yellow film which powders readily. The egg must not be allowed to coagulate during the drying process, as this would make the dried egg useless for baking: the usual temperature in drying is below 51·5° C. (125° F.). This is well below coagulation temperature of 72° C. (161·6°

F.), but it is also below the temperature lethal for salmonellae, and the egg powder is not sterile.

All bulk liquid egg must now be pasteurized in Britain. The pasteurization temperature is 64·4° C. (148° F.), and the liquid egg is exposed to this temperature for 2½ minutes. This would not cause coagulation of whole liquid egg nor of separated yolk, which begins to coagulate at about 71° C. (160° F.). It is therefore very desirable that whole egg or egg yolk should be pasteurized before drying.

Separated egg white (known when dried as crystal albumen) begins to coagulate around 63·3° C. (146° F.), which is below the temperature used for pasteurizing bulk liquid egg and such pasteurization would spoil the product. A lower temperature of 57·2° C. to 57·8° C. (135° F. to 136° F.) for a longer time may be effective, for salmonellae are killed at 55° C. in an hour (p. 30). Egg white is difficult to pasteurize after drying, but exposure to a temperature of 54·4° C. (130° F.) for days on end has been tried and may be effective. Although conditions have been greatly improved there must still be some uncertainty about the safety of some egg products. The key to success is to find some way of pasteurizing whole or separated eggs before drying which will not affect the baking properties of the dried product.

Milk

Germs are very fond of milk. The germ of tuberculosis used to be very common in cattle in Britain and many cases of bone tuberculosis in children were caused through drinking infected milk. Nowadays as a result of strict veterinary control of herds, tuberculosis is a rare disease in cattle in Britain, and milk-borne tuberculosis is now almost unknown. Typhoid fever has often been caused by drinking raw milk: one outbreak in a town in England affected over 500 people in 1936. Undulant fever (also known as Malta fever) is another disease that can be caused through drinking milk. Cases still occur in Britain. Food-poisoning germs such as salmonellae or staphylococci may get into milk and multiply in it, and, in the past, even outbreaks of scarlet fever and diphtheria have been spread by milk.

There are two things essential in producing safe milk: these are clean production *and* heat treatment. Clean production alone will not produce safe milk, for germs do not mind whether milk is clean or dirty, so long as they can get into it; but, of course, if production methods are scrupulously clean, germs have less chance of getting in. Heat treatment by pasteurization destroys all disease germs, and it is the only way of guaranteeing that milk is safe. Milk may be sold as *Untreated* only if it comes from cows that have been proved by tests to be free of tuberculosis: to get a licence to produce such milk, the dairy farmer must maintain very strict standards of cleanliness and herd hygiene. Such milk used to be sold as *Tuberculin Tested* milk: it is very clean milk and there are no tuberculosis germs in it. Other germs can get in, in spite of all the precautions the farmer can take. Such milk reaches a high standard of purity, but it is absolutely safe *only if it is pasteurized*. (For pasteurization processes see p. 170.)

Pasteurized milk can be contaminated after pasteurization. The cap of the bottle may be fouled and some germs may get into the bottle as it is opened. Most contamination occurs after the bottle is opened and the milk poured into other containers. There is nothing magic about pasteurized milk: the heat kills any disease germs present in the milk before heating, but germs that get in later can flourish in the pasteurized milk. Milk should therefore be handled with great care, covered from dust and stored in a refrigerator.

Dried milk. Dried milk powder is liquid milk from which the moisture is driven off by the spray or roller method as described for dried eggs (p. 102). The temperature is too low to kill all germs, but milk for drying is first pasteurized and the drying process then results in a safe milk. The milk powder is produced and packed under very careful factory conditions, but germs may get into the powder after the tin or packet is opened. They cannot multiply because the powder is too dry, but when water is added to reconstitute the milk the germs can multiply in it if it is left at room temperature. Obviously milk should not be reconstituted till required for cooking: if it must be made earlier, it should be stored in a refrigerator.

104

Evaporated and condensed milks. These are milks from which part of the moisture has been removed by heating under a vacuum. Only pasteurized milk is used and so these milks when canned are safe. Once the can is opened, germs can enter. In evaporated milk they can multiply quickly, unless it is kept at refrigerator temperature, but in sweetened condensed milk the high sugar content makes the milk almost self-sterilizing and bacteria cannot multiply in it.

To sum up, milk can be an ideal medium for disease germs to multiply in, and milk can therefore spread disease: but if milk is produced under good hygienic conditions, heat-treated and then kept carefully it is a safe nutritious food.

Cream

Cream contains most of the fat of milk and, as a medium for germs to grow in, it is very similar to milk. Cream can be separated from milk after pasteurization, or the cream itself can be pasteurized before or after bottling, so that cream should be as safe as milk. Unfortunately this is not so, for there are no legal requirements for the production of cream. A great deal of contamination may take place after the cream is pasteurized, for it is often sent to retailers in cans, and bottled or put in cartons in the shop. The cream which eventually reaches the bakery or the kitchen may be far from sterile. In one survey of over 600 samples of cream bought in shops, more than 200 failed the chemical test for purity. As cream is handled a lot in the kitchen or bakery, and often added to cakes or trifles long before they are eaten, any germs present have plenty of time to multiply, and food poisoning may follow (p. 205).

Artificial cream. The term 'artificial cream' covers a wide variety of products and preparations. At one end artificial cream may contain all the protein, fat and carbohydrate of dairy cream and, at the other, be compounded of water, starches, vegetable oil and other substances which never issued from a cow's udder. It can therefore be a wholesome and delicious addition to a ravishing sweet; on the other hand, it may be only a germ-contaminated emulsion squeezed over some soggy cake or sponge. It might be more logical to keep the term 'artificial cream' for products that are made from milk constituents, for example dried milk and butter, and to use the term 'synthetic cream' for those that contain none, but this is not the normal practice.

All artificial cream offered for sale must be clearly labelled 'artificial cream'. More important than a label are the contents and preparation of the cream. A good product is one made from dried milk, butter and sugar, and pasteurized in the factory. Such a cream can be as high in food value as fresh dairy cream, and as far as germ contamination is concerned, it is often much safer, for the standard of hygiene in artificial cream factories is now very high, and a can of branded artificial cream is a thoroughly satisfactory product. Other artificial creams are made from sugar, fat and eggs, and here the danger is from contaminated egg: if bulk liquid egg is used it must be pasteurized (p. 103) and is safe, but imported dried egg might not be.

Cream fillings. Various butter creams are made by confectioners and cooks in their own bakeries and kitchens. These may be made from sugar syrup, egg yolk and butter, or from egg yolks, fresh cream, sugar and butter and flavoured in many ways. Praline cream is butter cream with almond powder beaten into it, mocha cream is flavoured with coffee, while Plombières cream has liqueur added at the last moment. All these creams involve some degree of heating, but there is a good deal of whipping and beating during cooling, and the heating would not be enough to destroy germs that were present at the beginning or got in during these processes. Cold cream fillings can be made by beating icing sugar into fresh dairy cream, or by mixing sugar with egg white and butter.

Marshmallow and gelatin. A rich cake filling is made from mixing marshmallow with egg white and adding it to beaten butter and milk powder. Marshmallow itself is made from dissolved agar-agar or gelatin mixed with egg whites and sugar. Gelatin is manufactured from animal bone or hide which may well be contaminated with salmonellae: these are likely to be destroyed by heat during manufacture, but re-contamination may occur later when the gel has cooled. Agar-agar is not an animal product but is derived from seaweed: it is not contaminated at source, but if germs do get on it, they grow readily (p. 59).

All these fillings contain materials that may be contaminated with germs at the onset—egg, dairy cream or gelatin. The greatest danger lies, however, in contamination during and after preparation: the air may contain germs in dust. Tables and other working surfaces may have a coating of germs, but above all, plant and utensils may become contaminated by one batch of material and, if these are not thoroughly cleansed, germs can multiply in any film of cream left in them, and grossly contaminate future batches. All the handling, of course, lays these creams open to contamination from a human source, and staphylococci from confectioner's nose or fingers have caused outbreaks of food poisoning in this way (p. 212).

Cornflour filling. Synthetic cake filling can be made with water, cornflour, margarine or cooking fat, egg yolk and sugar. This is a nutritious food though it has no claim to be regarded as cream. The cornflour is thoroughly cooked, the fat or margarine is added at 65° C. (130° F.), still above the lethal point for food-poisoning germs, but the egg yolk is added when the mixture has cooled to 45° C. (130° F.) which is well below the lethal point. The main danger, however, is in contamination after preparation, for this filling is a good medium for germs.

Butter, margarine and fat

Germs find it difficult to digest fat. A few uncommon germs do produce an enzyme called lipase which breaks down fat into simpler substances which they can then use as food, but this does not apply to any of the food-poisoning germs. Very occasionally the germ of brucellosis or Malta fever (p. 83) has been found in butter and, more rarely, the germs of typhoid fever and tuberculosis; but these are epidemiological curiosities, not examples of common methods of spread. Moreover, butter is now made almost always from pasteurized milk, so that even these minute dangers are removed.

There is evidence that some fats and fatty acids are germicidal, that is they destroy germs, and it is certainly true that germs find life in a fatty medium very uncomfortable and cannot survive in it for long. This does not mean that one can be careless, for if butter or fat were contaminated at a late stage of preparation a few germs might survive and cause infection; but apart from these rare risks, butter and fat can be regarded as safe and wholesome foods.

Margarine is prepared by blending fat free milk with vegetable oils derived mainly from nuts—groundnuts, coconuts, and palm kernels are the commonest—sometimes whale oil is added to the blend. Every effort is made in the manufacture to reproduce the physical properties of butter. Spreading factor can in fact be controlled in margarine more easily than in butter, which is often too soft in summer and too hard in winter. As regards nutritional value the fats of margarine equal those of butter, and when vitamins are added to margarine there is no difference between the food values of the two. The only factor that eludes the manufacturer is the subtle flavour of butter. As regards freedom from germs, margarine is even safer than butter, for most of its constituents are of vegetable not animal origin and it is manufactured under conditions of maximum hygiene. Yet the prejudice against margarine persists, and people regard butter as a natural, but margarine as an artificial food. It is difficult to understand how butter can be regarded as a more natural food for man than margarine, for butter is prepared entirely from cow's milk, which is intended by nature to be sucked from the cow's udder by its calf, whereas margarine is derived mainly from the fruits of the earth. The caveman with whom this book started probably ate nuts, but he certainly never ate butter.

Flour

Flour consists of 70 to 75 per cent carbohydrate, 8 to 12 per cent protein, less than 1 per cent fat, traces of cellulose and mineral salts and about 14 per cent moisture. It is much too dry for germs, and bacterial food poisoning has never been caused by flour.

Chemical food poisoning has occurred on several occasions due to contamination with dangerous chemicals in transit or storage (p. 77).

Cornflour is derived from maize. Like flour it is dry and unsuitable for germ life. When heated with water or milk to over 75° C. (167° F.) it gelatinizes, and as it cools, it sets as a jelly. Such a jelly is sterile but, if it became contaminated later, germs could grow readily on it.

Rice flour is derived from the rice plant. It is often used as a dusting powder on confectionery and cakes. It forms a jelly in the same way as cornflour. It is safe when dry, but a good medium for germs when moist.

Arrowroot is not a cereal but is derived from the thick root, or rhizome, of several plants. The story that American Indians used root flour to heal arrow wounds seems to be untrue: the Indian word for root flour is araruta and has nothing to do with English arrows. Arrowroot is used to make milk puddings, moulds and blancmanges. It is also used, by boiling with water and sugar, to make jelly for pouring over flans and tarts. It is sterile when prepared, but may be contaminated after it cools.

Sugar, honey and jam

Most germs require some of the simpler sugars such as glucose or lactose for food, but only in weak solutions. They cannot survive in strong concentrations. A strong solution of a substance such as sugar or salt always draws fluid from weaker solutions. Germs are composed mainly of water with low concentrations of salts and sugars in them (as indeed the human body is), and if germs are placed in a strong solution of sugar or salt, water is drawn out of their bodies and they die of thirst or dehydration. This is the principle used in the preservation of food by salts and sugar (p. 174).

Jam and honey contain very high concentrations of sugar in solution and germs cannot survive in such conditions. Sometimes a mould grows on the top of a jar of honey or jam, but this is because there has been some condensation of water at the top of the jar which lowers the concentration of sugar in the surface layer—low enough for moulds and yeasts, but still much too high for other germs. Sweetened condensed milk is another product with such high sugar concentration that germs cannot live in it. Sugar and all preparations containing strong solutions of it are, as far as germ contamination is concerned, very safe foods.

Cocoa and chocolate

Cocoa is a powder obtained by roasting and crushing cocoa beans: these grow in large pods in cocoa trees. The powder contains a substance similar to the caffeine of tea and coffee and has a stimulating effect on the brain: this substance is a stimulant drug, not a food. The powder also contains cocoa-butter which is a food with a high calorie value. A cup of cocoa therefore has food value of its own, whereas a cup of coffee or tea has none apart from that supplied by the added milk and sugar, but, of course, there are only one or two teaspoons of cocoa in a cup so that the amount of nutriment is quite small.

In the crushing and roasting process a good deal of cocoa-butter is extracted from the beans though some still remains in the cocoa powder. To make chocolate, more cocoa-butter is added to the cocoa powder and the mixture is blended with sugar. (Confectioners require a very pliable chocolate and this is produced by adding still more cocoa-butter to the blend.) Plain chocolate contains approximately 30 per cent fat and 60 per cent sugar. Milk chocolate has dried or condensed milk added to it: this raises the fat content and lowers the sugar content. From the safety point of view, the concentrations of fat and sugar in all chocolate, as well as the heating during roasting and blending, guarantee a germ-free product.

Coconut. Coconut, as used in confectionery, is derived from the dried fleshy part of the fruit of the coco-palm. It contains up to 50 per cent fat and, being of vegetable origin, should be free of any germs derived from animals. Unfortunately the standard of hygiene practised in the harvesting and drying of the coconuts in tropical countries has been in the past deplorably low, and the dried coconut has been contaminated with salmonellae of human and animal origin. These germs probably find it hard to multiply in the desiccated coconut, but when this is scattered on some sponge, gateau or trifle the germs find the moisture they need there and multiply quickly. Outbreaks of food poisoning and paratyphoid fever have been caused in this way (p. 208). Fortunately the standards of hygiene in the producing countries have been raised and the danger of contamination greatly reduced. Importers in Britain also subject the coconut to heat sterilization, so that coconut is now usually a safe product.

The story of coconut food poisoning is important, because it emphasizes how every process in food production must be supervized and scrutinized. Time, money, legislation and care are required to produce a safe end-product, yet all may be undone at the last moment by a few flakes of nuts contaminated some thousands of miles across the ocean.

The Sweets Trolley

Having examined the constituents, now let us look at the sweets trolley. It is certainly tempting, but is it safe?

The first thing the food hygienist notes is that many of the articles on the trolley contain materials on which germs grow readily: there is plenty of carbohydrate and protein and plenty of moisture. The second point he notes is that the trolley is wheeled into the restaurant before the beginning of the meal and remains there for several hours, so that there is also plenty of warmth and time. What he cannot see is whether germs are present or not; this he can only judge if he knows what has gone into each article and under what conditions it has been prepared. What might his conclusions be?

Gateaux, eclairs and sponges

All these have been prepared from flour, eggs, milk and sugar, and, fresh from the oven, are free from food-poisoning germs. There are three dangers thereafter. The first is that some form of artificial cream or other filling is usually added and this may be contaminated with germs (p. 105). The filling moistens the dry sponge or batter and the germs may then multiply there in great comfort. The second danger is that the air and dust of the kitchen or bakehouse may be full of germs and these may alight on the food after baking. The third danger, one common to all foods, is that a human carrier may contaminate the food after baking. In all three cases, the germs, once on these foods, will find the conditions very suitable for multiplication.

Trifles and Meringues

A trifle is virtually the same thing, from a germ's point of view, as a gateau or sponge: a trifle is moister and so easier to grow on. Trifle left-over is an ideal medium for germs. At room temperature, a few staphylococci could multiply to millions overnight: in a refrigerator the numbers would not increase. Alcohol is an excellent disinfectant, but the amount of sherry in a trifle tends to be meagre and would not discourage determined germs.

Meringues are made from white of egg and sugar. The more egg white used, the lighter is the meringue. They may be used as fillings, coverings or dried as a shell. They may be made in the cold, or baked in the oven. If the whites of fresh shell eggs are used there is very little danger, but bulked egg white (crystal albumen) is not always free from germs (p. 103) and there is therefore some risk in the cold process. Meringue shells are produced by baking at 121° C. (250° F.), a temperature which dries the meringue but does not caramelize the sugar: it would also kill any germs present in the mix. The only danger from shell meringues lies in the filling: if it is contaminated, the meringue is no longer a safe confection.

Charlottes, fools, mousses, jellies and blancmange

The factor common to all these sweets is that they are largely uncooked. Charlotte russe, for example, is prepared by beating cold custard with gelatin and whipped cream: the eggs in the custard, the gelatin and the cream are all liable to be contaminated

112

with germs (p. 106). (Apple charlotte is a very different sweet composed of bread, butter, apple and sugar and thoroughly cooked in the oven.) Fools are cold fruit purées whipped with sugar and cream, and dessert mousses have a base of chantilly cream (double cream plus sugar and vanilla) with chocolate or other flavouring or fruit purée added. In both fools and mousses the cream may be suspect. The basis of jellies is gelatin. This is dissolved in a little cold water, then boiling water and the flavourings are added and the jelly left to set. If salmonellae were present in the gelatin, this degree of heating would hardly kill them. Blancmange originally was prepared from pounded sweet and bitter almonds set in a mould with sugar, water and isinglass. Today blancmange usually consists of a cold cornflour pudding variously flavoured. It is a rather insipid dish, but germs, if they got into the cold mould, could certainly flourish in it.

Custards and caramels

Baked custards and caramel creams depend for setting on the coagulation of egg. This requires a temperature of at least 72° C. (161·6° F.) and this is well above the temperature required to kill food-poisoning germs (p. 30). These custards and creams are therefore safe when first prepared: if left to cool and stored before being served, germs might gain entry and would multiply rapidly.

Pies, tarts and flans

In Britain a tart has two crusts and a flan only one. In America an English tart would be called a pie, and an English flan a tart. Names apart, they are the same things and consist of pastry with fruit filling. Most fruits are acid and germs do not multiply in acid. Moreover, the more acid the environment the more quickly are germs destroyed by heat. Fruit tarts and flans are therefore very unlikely to harbour food-poisoning germs when they come out of the oven. A jelly is usually added to flans after they are baked: this may be made of gelatin (p. 106) or of cornflour or arrowroot (p. 109) and there is some risk of germs being added then, but,

113

even so, they are unlikely to multiply in the acid medium. A more likely danger lies in the whipped cream (natural or artificial) which may be used to decorate a flan, or the cream which is served to eat along with the tart.

Ice-cream

What exactly is ice-cream? The only exact definition is a physical one—ice-cream is an oil in water emulsion. The oil phase consists of fat and the water phase contains milk solids, sugar and flavouring. This oil-in-water emulsion is known as the 'mix'. In Britain the mix must contain 5 per cent fat and $7\frac{1}{2}$ per cent milk solids. If the ice-cream is to be sold as 'dairy ice-cream', the fat must be milk fat: but in 'ordinary' ice-cream this is not the case and the fat is usually vegetable fat. To improve the stability and texture of the ice-cream, emulsifying and stabilizing agents are added. The commonest are glyceryl monostearate and gelatin. These keep the texture firm but not too hard, and prevent too rapid melting and the formation of large crystals. The result is an even, velvety, icy substance which melts smoothly in the mouth. It is of high calorie value and, though sold in millions of tons for its cooling properties, it must, when digested, add to the production of body heat. At the moment of consumption it is accepted eagerly as a refreshing frozen sweet, without a thought for calories. Unfortunately before it is frozen, it is a highly acceptable food for germs. Unless precautions are taken, ice-cream can cause disease and there have been large outbreaks of food poisoning, typhoid and paratyphoid fever caused in this way.

Heat treatment. Under the Ice-cream (Heat Treatment, etc.) Regulations of 1959 ice-cream mix must be heated and must conform to other time and temperature requirements. The principles are those applicable to the safe handling of any food—heat to kill germs, quick cooling to prevent germs entering and multiplying at intermediate temperatures, and cool storage till required. The legislation allows three methods of pasteurizing the mix. It may be heated and held (*a*) at 65·6° C. (150° F.) for 30 minutes, (*b*) at 71·4° C. (160° F.) for 10 minutes or (*c*) at 79·4° C. (175° F.) for 15 seconds. After methods (*a*) and (*b*), the mix must be cooled within 1½ hours to 7·2° C. (45° F.), and it must be kept at or below this temperature till it is frozen. The temperature after freezing must not rise above −2·2° C. (28° F.): if it does, the mix must be re-treated. After method (*c*) the mix may be transferred, with aseptic precautions, into sterile, air-tight containers, and the law does not require that it be kept at a specified low temperature before freezing.

Soft ice-cream. These pasteurized or sterilized mixes are known as 'soft ice-creams' and are supplied as such to restaurants and retailers who are responsible for freezing it. A mix may be evaporated after heat treatment and sold as a cold mix powder: after it is reconstituted it must be frozen within 1 hour.

Safety

Ice-cream mix is a good medium for germ growth. The most likely source of infection is a human carrier of staphylococci or of typhoid or paratyphoid germs. These germs, if they are given time and warmth, multiply rapidly in the mix and the staphylococci produce toxin. Subsequent freezing destroys neither the germs nor the staphylococcal toxin. Before legislation made heat-treatment compulsory, ice-cream was a dangerous article of food. With the heat treatment, rapid cooling and freezing required by law it is now one of the safest. The dangers that remain arise at two sources: (*a*) in the manufacturer's plant and (*b*) in the handling of the unfrozen mix after it has left the factory.

Defects in the plant arise from incomplete cleaning and sterilizing somewhere along the processing line. If this occurs in the cooler or vats after pasteurization, contamination of the mix occurs, and although the temperature might be too low to allow much multiplication, enough germs, especially typhoid germs, might persist to cause serious trouble. A pasteurization plant is not a self-sterilizing unit: it must be maintained and serviced by an engineer who understands not only the mechanical aspects but also the hygienic work the plant is required to do.

A modern ice-cream factory is usually run on very satisfactory lines and high standards of bacteriological purity are achieved. This is true also of most restaurants and retailers, but here the human factor becomes important. Unless all utensils used for storing the soft ice-cream, for reconstituting cold-mix powder and for final freezing of the mix are cleaned thoroughly and sterilized between uses, contamination may occur. If there is any failure to observe temperature requirements, such contamination could have serious results. To handle ice-cream safely a retailer requires intelligence and some knowledge of hygienic requirements. These qualities are not always prominent in some branches of the trade, and supervision by public health inspectors is necessary. As stated above, ice-cream properly prepared and distributed is one of our safest foods, but germs are always ready to take advantage of human carelessness or ignorance.

Fruit

Fruit is another safe food, for most fruits are too acid for germs to thrive on. If the skin of fruit is dusty it is common sense to wash it, but dipping fruit, especially grapes, in a bowl of water on the table before eating it is of no value. If germs are present on the skin some would be washed into the water which would then become a source of further contamination. Fresh fruit is wholesome food and can be eaten without worrying about food poisoning.

Canned fruit has never caused bacterial food poisoning: germs are readily killed in an acid medium by the heat of the canning process (p. 40). Dried fruit may be contaminated with food-poisoning germs if the standard of hygiene in the exporting country is low: the germs cannot multiply in the dry, acid fruit, but if this is left to soak in water, any germs present would readily multiply. No outbreaks due to this cause have been reported, probably because the dried fruit requires thorough cooking.

If one has any qualms about a batch of fruit, it can be washed in water containing 60 to 80 parts per million chlorine: this will destroy any food-poisoning germs present.

Cheese and Biscuits

Cheese

Cheese is a highly concentrated food made from milk: 1 pint of milk forms about 2 oz. of cheese. To make cheese from milk, a culture of lactic acid bacteria (the starter culture) is added to the milk: these bacteria attack the lactose of the milk (milk sugar) and convert it into lactic acid which causes souring of the milk. The milk is now warmed and rennet is added. This causes a curd to form and this curd is the future cheese. The liquid or whey is allowed to drain off and later the curd is pressed to squeeze out as much whey as possible. The cheese is then left to mature for several months. Cream cheese is made in the same way, except that it is not pressed and so has a more open texture and retains more moisture. Moulds can grow in some cheeses and help to mature them. Stilton, for example, is a mould-matured cheese.

Safety

Two points can be made at once. (1) If cheese is made from pasteurized milk it is safe. All commercially produced cheese in Britain is made from pasteurized milk and this is true of many foreign countries too. (2) The mature, hard cheese is much too dry to support the growth of germs.

If cheese is made from raw milk, germs in the milk may grow in the cheese. In fact, such germs can displace the starter germs. Staphylococci are often present in raw milk and cheese made from such milk may be teeming with staphylococci, and outbreaks of food poisoning have been caused in this way (p. 189). Cream cheeses made from raw milk are especially dangerous, for the extra moisture in the finished cheese allows germs to multiply. Germs other than the common food-poisoning germs may be present in such cream cheeses, for example brucellae, the germs of undulant and Malta fever. (All milk in Malta is now pasteurized and one can eat the delicious Malta cream cheeses with confidence and enjoyment.) The main danger comes from home-made cheese, for contamination with germs from the cheese-maker can

117

readily occur. Commercially prepared cheese can normally be regarded as wholesome and safe.

Biscuits

The diner who is also a food hygienist can relax completely when he comes to this final article on the menu, for as far as food poisoning is concerned, biscuits are blameless. A biscuit contains only 5 per cent water. This crisp dryness is for the diner a biscuit's main attraction, but germs will have none of it. They will put up with a good deal in their efforts to survive, but not with this degree of dryness. Our food hygienist may therefore munch his fill of biscuits, confident that whatever risks he may have taken with earlier items in the menu, he runs none at all with the last.

So we come to the end of the repast, a hazardous journey. From start to finish, the diner can do nothing to fend off hidden dangers, for the safety of the food he eats depends on the history of its production, distribution and preparation before it is brought to the table. Most meals are thoroughly safe and wholesome, and food poisoning hits the headlines and radio and TV news only because it is an uncommon occurrence, and therefore is news. It should, of course, never occur at all. It is always due to some fault in the production, distribution or preparation of food, and these faults are preventable. Yet nearly all the food items examined in these two chapters have been concerned in food-poisoning incidents. That, of course, is why we have examined them. Only if one understands how food poisoning occurs can one hope to prevent its occurring again and again. A little learning may be a dangerous thing, but, in the practice of food hygiene, a little knowledge makes for safety.

14

Reflections on Some 'Plats du Jour'

'Dry bible' and lamsiekte

Animals as well as man may suffer from food poisoning. We have already seen (p. 50) that food pellets fed to animals may be contaminated with salmonellae, and that the animals eating these contract salmonella infection. Out in the wilds, animals sometimes run serious risks from the food they eat. On the South African veldt, for example, when the grass is old and seeding, its mineral content drops and grazing cattle develop a craving for phosphorus. They satisfy this by eating carcass debris and bones and especially the shells of dead tortoises which lie abundantly on the veldt. Inside the shell there is a spongy lining, and if germs from the soil get into it they find conditions ideal for multiplying. One of these germs is *Clostridium botulinum* and the cattle develop a disease known as lamsiekte: the symptoms are weakness of the limbs and paralysis of the muscles of the jaw, tongue and throat, very similar to the symptoms of human botulism (p. 46). There is another disease known by the extraordinary name of 'dry bible' which affects cattle and sheep in Australia: they get it from eating the decaying corpses of rabbits which are infected from the soil with botulism germs. In both cases the germ grows under the baking sun of the bush or veldt, but it can also flourish in the cool, damp shade under decaying rushes on the edge of North American lakes, and hundreds of thousands of ducks have died from a paralytic disease known as 'duck sickness' caused by *Clostridium botulinum.*

The circumstances under which these animals are poisoned may be odd and unexpected, but at least they are beyond the control of the animals. Man, on the other hand, is such an eccentric animal

119

that he may by his own contrivances produce conditions for germs to grow in his food which are quite as bizarre as any that occur in nature. He may do so in a native settlement, or in the kitchen of an international hotel.

Utjak and izushi

Utjak is an Eskimo delicacy. It is made from pieces of seal flippers kept soaking in oil till they rot and acquire a flavour which the Eskimo finds irresistible. Unfortunately *Clostridium botulinum* also likes decaying seal meat, and whole families have been found dead in their igloo after eating their favourite food. Izushi is a Japanese dish: it is composed of raw fish, rice and vegetables. The fish is soaked for four or five days until it becomes suitably tainted; it is then mixed with the cooked rice and vegetables and left to ferment for three or four weeks until it is ripe and ready for eating. It is sure to be highly flavoured, but if the germs of botulism are present in the fish they multiply in the anaerobic conditions of this concoction and many deaths have been caused in Japan by eating contaminated izushi. On the Pacific Coast of North America the Indians are fond of salmon-egg cheese; they prepare it in several ways but, in all, the salmon eggs are allowed to ferment for several weeks, and this process produces low oxygen tension which favours the growth of *Clostridium botulinum*. The Indians may eat this *pièce de résistance* with great relish, but they are likely to die from botulism as an aftermath.

Civilized gourmandism

All the above may seem outlandish preparations, but are *marinades crues* very different from utjak? In winter, according to one authority, the raw meat may be left in the marinade (a spicy mixture of wine and oil) for 5 to 6 days, but in summer 24 to 48 hours is enough! And how about *Purée de cervelles d'agneau*? This is a preparation of sieved lamb's brains, mixed with white sauce and cream, and used as a garnish for soft-boiled eggs or as a filling for pastry cases. Young hares, according to another authority, should be hung unpaunched for a week before cooking: the blood of the

120

hare may be added later to the sauce but, if so, the sauce must not be allowed to boil or the blood will curdle. Venison may smell rather high if kept for the recommended time; it may then be washed 'in warm water', but some gamey flavour is desirable. Partridges should be hung for 10 to 14 days to obtain 'full flavour', and the same authority suggests that capercailzies should be buried in the ground for a few days before using. Game birds in general should be hung undrawn and unplucked till 'feathers can be pulled out easily'; if feathers are difficult to pluck, 'hang a little longer'. Fortunately game birds, even when high and their feathers falling out, are usually thoroughly cooked before being eaten. However, the marinades and the purée are eaten cold. The civilized gourmet in some elegant restaurant takes risks with them not very different from the Eskimo in his igloo.

Part 3

15

Food Hygiene: The Problems

By ignorance we know not things necessary: by errour
we know them falsely.

Burton, *Anatomy of Melancholy*

Food poisoning is not caused by food, but by germs in or on it. These germs are living things and, like man himself, they survive and multiply only when conditions favour them. Man dies of starvation if he cannot get food, he may freeze to death if he lacks clothes or shelter, or he may die of heat and thirst if he cannot reach water. In some respects germs are tougher than man. They can tolerate being frozen for months on end and can live in dry dust for years. On the other hand many of them die rapidly at a temperature not much above that of a hot bath or shower. We can destroy germs by making things too hot for them, but they can elude us in the cold interior of a refrigerator or in a dry dusty crack in a bakehouse or kitchen. To defeat germs, we must remember all we know about them.

In Part 1 of this book we have traced the passage of germs from the stock farm or poultry house, or even from across the sea, through abattoirs, poultry plants, food factories, shops and bakeries till they reach our kitchens, and from there get on to our dining table. We must now study how to interrupt their adventurous life. Three considerations must guide our practice, all three derived from facts examined in Part 1 of this book.

1. Food-poisoning germs are often present on food when it reaches the kitchen. This is especially true of raw meat which may be contaminated with salmonellae or *Clostridium welchii* (p. 65). Germs may have contaminated the food at any point between the

farm and the kitchen: they may indeed have reached the farm from across the sea.

Germs may be present in the kitchen itself, and can easily get on and into food. These germs may have got into the air and dust of the kitchen from some infected food and may persist there for a long time (p. 64). They may be brought in on sacks of vegetables or on boots and shoes (p. 65). Probably the most dangerous source of all is the food handler in the kitchen: he may be a carrier of staphylococci, salmonellae, shigellae (dysentery germs) or *Clostridium welchii* (p. 65).

A kitchen may be sparkling clean, but it should always be regarded as a dangerous area. *Germs, remember, are invisible. All that glisters is not gold, and 'clean' and 'safe' do not mean the same thing.*

2. Food that is good for man is also good for germs. Given a little warmth and moisture, germs revel and multiply in many foods, but they die in heat and stop multiplying in the cold, so they like to get into cooked food that is left for a long time in the nice, warm atmosphere of a kitchen or cupboard. They have a weakness for left-overs, pies, creams, sweets and cooked meats, and they can build up deadly populations in them.

3. Germs cannot get on to food by themselves. They depend on the carelessness or ignorance of man at some stage of their journey. In the kitchen they look to the food handler to help them on their way. He often assists them unawares.

It is easy to state simple facts such as the above, but not so easy to practise what they imply. To prevent the spread of infection in animals before and after slaughter could involve great changes in animal husbandry, veterinary methods and slaughter-house practice. It would also require vast sums of money. This does not mean the problems need not be tackled. They must be, but one should know the size of a problem beforehand. As food hygienists we must be aware of these problems and press for their solution, though it is not our job to tackle them. The spread of infection in food factories, bakeries, shops and kitchens *is* our concern, and it is our job to do everything possible to prevent it.

The most important thing is to be aware. This means understanding the facts given in this book. Stainless-steel utensils are fine in a kitchen, but if there is a thin, almost invisible film of cream inside a stainless-steel mixing bowl, it becomes a dangerous piece of equipment. A refrigerator is essential in a kitchen for keeping food cold and preventing germs multiplying, but if a food handler places contaminated food in it, he may easily get the germs on his hands and transfer them to other food in the refrigerator. These may start to multiply when the food is taken out next day. It may appear hygienic to wipe plates or glasses with a clean cloth, but the cloth, though clean, may be covered with germs. A glass display cabinet protects food against the entry of germs, but if the food is already contaminated when placed in it, the cabinet becomes an incubator for the germs. One could go on adding examples and we will have to look at more examples in the next few chapters, but we do not need to examine and assess the good and bad points of elaborate factory or kitchen equipment. Awareness is a much better protection against the spread of infection than a battery of the latest equipment. This is not to decry good equipment: we cannot have too much of it in our shops and kitchens, but none of it will protect against ignorance. We must understand the mechanism of any equipment or machinery we use: but it is much more important to understand the mechanism of the spread of infection.

16

Food Hygiene: From Farm to Factory

The young infant

When an infant is in hospital great care is taken to avoid infection. Its feeds are sterilized, and everything around it that might harbour germs is disinfected frequently. It is often nursed in a separate room or cubicle which is carefully sealed from outside contamination, and when the nurse leaves the cot-side, she takes precautions, with her clothes and her person, to make sure that she cannot carry germs to another infant. These measures are very successful, but, if there is the slightest slip, cross-infection can occur.

The young animal

Calves are just as liable as infants to catch infections. In fact, a common infection of calves, known as 'scours', is a very similar disease to gastro-enteritis of babies, and is often caused by the same family of germs, the escherichiae (p. 26). However, the conditions under which calves are kept are very different from the isolation cubicle of an infant, and if these germs get into the cowshed they find it easy to spread from one animal to another.

Salmonellae too are common germs of farmyard animals. They cause disease in calves and piglets and also in adult cows and pigs. Many of the latter become permanent carriers, so that the germs which get into the cowsheds and pig sties eventually reach the slaughter-house floor, contaminating our meat and pork (p. 55). Young chicks, too, are very easily infected, and the germs may contaminate whole hatcheries. When the chicks move on to the broiler farms they take the infection with them, where it can persist till the birds go to the poultry plant, and in the end thousands of dressed carcasses in the deep-freeze may harbour salmonellae. The next stage is food poisoning in those who eat the poultry (p. 193) or the meat.

It is easy to be critical of such a state of affairs, but not so easy to remedy it. The asepsis of an isolation cubicle cannot be attained in a cowshed, yet a good deal can be achieved once the need is realized. When farmers became aware of the advantages of producing clean milk, the standard of hygiene in milking byres rose so high that the term *milking parlours* came into use. The important word in that sentence is *aware*. The dangers of salmonellosis are not so obvious on the stock or poultry farm as are the dangers of germs in the milking parlour. The infection is often silent, and it is difficult to persuade people to spend time and money on something they cannot see. It is much more difficult to get them to spend money on something which appears to do no harm. Thus salmonellae may spread widely among chicks and adult birds without causing any illness in them or interfering with their growth, and no one knows there is anything wrong with the birds till an outbreak of food poisoning occurs in the human beings who eat them (p. 193). Nevertheless if salmonellosis hits a farm in an acute form, killing off calves and older cows, the owner of the stock will do anything to prevent a recurrence.

Impracticable and idealistic as it may seem, the aim must be to achieve inside farm buildings and poultry houses conditions in which germs find it difficult to spread. This involves sound building construction, the use of impermeable materials for floors and stalls, good ventilation, adequate water supply and drainage and the exclusion of vermin. It also requires informed personnel who understand what all these requirements are for, and who are therefore careful to see to the thorough and regular cleansing of the premises and the provision of maximum comfort for the animals. A clean cowshed may still not be free of dangerous germs, but there are likely to be far fewer than in a dirty one. The rearing of a calf is very similar to the rearing of an infant: they both thrive better when the standard of hygiene is high.

Animal food poisoning

The danger from infected feeding stuffs has already been mentioned (p. 50). Bone meal and meat-and-bone meal are often contaminated with salmonellae: fish meal and vegetable products such as cotton or groundnut cake, soya meal or copra are less often contaminated. These proteins are mixed with carbohydrates, roughage, minerals and vitamins to make a balanced animal food, and are usually fed as pellets. In the manufacture of the pellets the mixture is heated, and, if the temperature rises high enough, any salmonellae in it are killed. In some processes, however, the temperature does not reach 60° C. and will not kill the germs (p. 30). It is much better practice to sterilize the materials by heat before any mixing takes place, because clouds of dust are raised in the mixing, and this dust may contain germs and might easily settle on the pellets and re-contaminate them. Some countries have laws requiring sterilization of materials before pelleting, but in Britain

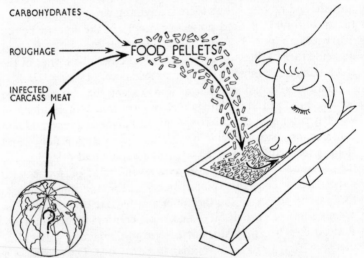

CARBOHYDRATES

ROUGHAGE

INFECTED CARCASS MEAT

FOOD PELLETS

Fig. 13. Animals may suffer from *compulsory* food poisoning. All feeding stuffs should be sterilized (p. 129)

130

and many other countries this is still not the case. It is largely a matter of economics and organization, but there can be no excuse for feeding contaminated food to animals. This is one form of food poisoning which can be prevented. There is no excuse for allowing it to continue.

Antibiotics

Antibiotics are used a great deal in animal husbandry. In some way that is not understood, antibiotics added to the feed seem to help some young animals and birds to put on weight more quickly. Antibiotics are also used to prevent the spread of infection or to treat infected animals. The snag is that although in theory antibiotics should prove useful for these purposes, very often they do not work. This is especially true when the germ is a salmonella, either in animals or in man, yet vast quantities of antibiotics are given to try to deal with salmonella infections, usually with no effect. This might not matter, apart from the waste and the cost, but salmonellae and other intestinal germs develop resistance to antibiotics, and sometimes they can pass on this resistance to other germs. This is a highly complex matter which bacteriologists are studying very carefully, and it is now known that resistance has been passed on in this way to dangerous germs such as those that cause typhoid fever. In one big epidemic of typhoid fever in Mexico in 1972 the germ was resistant to chloramphenicol, the best antibiotic for the treatment of the disease. This transfer of resistance need not be further discussed here, but it is mentioned to show how difficult control of infection can be and how sometimes a method of attack which seems harmless and logical can lead to very unexpected dangers. Antibiotics do not solve the problems of the spread of infection.

Animals on the move

The hazards to which animals and birds are exposed when they undertake their last journey have already been described (p. 54). They suffer from 'stress' and 'shrinkage' (p. 53) and the level of

131

infection rises steeply. There is no doubt that the conditions under which the animals are herded and transported are responsible for this. A truck crammed with cattle or sheep, or a lorry loaded with crates of live birds is not a pleasant sight. There is scant attention to hygiene and also an element of brutality in the procedure: but man is a meat-eating animal, and to satisfy his carnivorous appetite, hundreds of thousands of other animals must be got to the abattoir or poultry plant, and there slaughtered and carved up for his food. Man is the consumer and must face these facts, but it is his duty, as well as being to his advantage, to ensure that the process is carried out as quickly and as cleanly as possible.

One of the most important factors in the spread of infection, both in animals and man, is the intensity of exposure to the germ. Thus, in human infections, people living in overcrowded conditions tend to suffer more from infections than those living in better houses. Infectious diseases are commoner in winter than in summer, possibly because people stay indoors more in winter, and so are exposed for longer periods to one another's germs. A third factor is the standard of hygiene: infectious diseases are much commoner in underdeveloped countries with poor sanitation. All these factors, overcrowding, time, and poor hygiene are equally important in the spread of infection in animals on the move. A good deal of discomfort is caused to these animals by bad timing. They may be held up in trucks in sidings, in lorries at markets, or in lairs at markets and abattoirs. These delays lead to overcrowding, to bad feeding and watering, and to gross soiling of the environment with faeces, all factors which give germs the opportunity to multiply and to spread from one animal to another.

Often those in charge of the animals have no knowledge at all of the danger of infection, but the law does take some notice of it, and the Slaughterhouse Regulations of 1967 made it an offence to keep animals in abattoir lairs for more than 72 hours before slaughter. However 72 hours is a long time if conditions are bad, and many animals may be infected before they reach the abattoir floor. From then on, the spread of infection can be more easily controlled, if only operators are aware that germs may be present and can spread through an abattoir, if given the chance. The chance is given by carelessness and ignorance. It can be prevented by awareness and care. It has already been stated that an abattoir can be as clean as an operating theatre (p. 56). This is an exaggeration, for in the killing area there are bound to be blood and debris, but in a well-designed abattoir these can be quickly drained away or removed, and, once the carcass is skinned, it can be hung, eviscerated, cooled and stored with such attention to hygiene that cross-contamination of one carcass with the germs of another can be prevented. On the other hand, in a bad abattoir, germs find life easy and spread so rapidly that knives, chopping-blocks and other equipment become contaminated, and salmonellae and other germs can be grown from swabs dipped in the abattoir drains (p. 204).

Poultry plants

A poultry plant in essence is a long building with a conveyor belt constantly moving through it. At one end live birds enter, and at the other, oven-ready carcasses come out. These go either direct to retail shops or into deep-freeze at the far end of the poultry plant. The processes involved are culling, killing, bleeding; plucking, eviscerating, and cooling; trussing, weighing and packing. Culling means the removal of birds that are obviously sick or diseased: the other terms explain themselves. Now, poultry may be heavily infected with germs, especially salmonellae, without showing any sign of disease (p. 129), and cross-contamination of carcasses can occur in the poultry plant if the design and working conditions are poor. Some poultry plants are little more than improvised packing sheds and in these it is impossible to maintain satisfactory hygiene, and germs can pass freely from one bird carcass to another. The final product, the table bird, is bacteriologically unfit for human consumption, though this may unfortunately not be known till after it has been eaten.

The most important point in a good poultry plant is that it should be large enough to deal with the number of birds passing through it. There must be no hold-up of carcasses at any stage.

The building should be well-ventilated so that dust from feathers and excreta does not accumulate, and built of impervious material so that walls and floors can be thoroughly washed. It should be so designed that, although the flow of carcasses is never halted, the various processes are carried out in areas structurally separated one from another: culling is separate from killing, killing from plucking, and plucking from eviscerating. The aim is that when the carcass is finally being trussed and packed, that part of the plant may be as free as possible from any contamination that might arise from the earlier processes. There must be a lavish supply of water, at least 3 to 5 gallons per bird, and this should be chlorinated so that there is a supply of free chlorine in the water during all wet processes. Feathers, droppings and inedible offals must be removed quickly from the main part of the plant, and there must be adequate provision for sterilizing crates and bins, preferably by steam, and for regularly washing down all immovable parts of the plant with detergents and disinfectants. A good poultry plant should be clean and sparkling, with white-tiled walls, plenty of light and well-washed floors: all fittings and equipment should be of metal, cleanly designed so that dirt and debris cannot collect in grooves and chinks. In such a poultry plant, cross contamination can be prevented. No other type of poultry plant should be tolerated.

In this chapter we have aimed at the ideal, the elimination of germs from our food on its way from farm to factory. Perhaps it is an ideal that cannot be achieved, but in our attack we are not tilting at innocent windmills, but engaging in very real bacterial warfare in which the greatest help to the enemy is ignorance on our side. 'He that voluntarily continues in ignorance is guilty of all the crimes which ignorance produces.' That was said by Dr. Johnson in the eighteenth century. Food hygienists could scarcely find a better motto today.

17

Food Hygiene: The Food Factory

We closed the last chapter on a note of idealism, and perhaps with the feeling that some of the factors leading to contamination of food were beyond our control. We begin this chapter on a sharp, practical note by stating that from now on the control of contamination is entirely in our hands. That last phrase, 'in our hands', should be in every food hygienist's mind, in both its figurative and its literal meaning.

Transport

We have seen that some of the meat leaving the abattoir may be covered with germs. These germs will contaminate anything they come in contact with, and this includes containers and vans. These should therefore be specially designed so that they can be easily cleaned and disinfected. The walls of vehicles should be lined with metal or plastic, and the joints must be sealed so that no blood, fat or other liquid can seep through. The floor must also be made of impermeable material: aluminium alloys, studded to prevent slipping, are often used. Where separate boxes or containers are used, these should also be made of metal or plastic and jointed securely. All vans and containers must be well ventilated, and also protected from dust and flies.

Disinfecting the ambulance

When an infectious patient is taken to hospital, the ambulance may require to be cleaned and disinfected thereafter, depending on the type of infection: often thorough airing and ventilating of the ambulance suffices. A van used for carrying meat from abattoir to factory is likely to be in a much more dangerous condition as regards infection than any ambulance, for blood and other juices full of germs drip from the meat, and the carcasses can swing against the walls on the journey. Germs, remember, are on the surface of abattoir meat: in a patient they are usually well inside his body. Ideally, vans used for carrying food should carry nothing else to avoid danger of spilling dangerous substances on the food (p. 77).

Hot and cold water must be available at departure points for the thorough cleansing of vehicles and containers. Hoses, detergents, brooms and buckets are all required. There must be a planned routine and plenty of time to do the job. Above all, the operators must be well informed so that they understand the importance of the job they are doing.

Factory design

A food factory should be bright, spacious and gleaming. Walls should be finished with a smooth, light, impervious and washable surface, and where they join ceiling and floor, the junction should be moulded or coved so that they are easily cleaned. Ceilings should be smooth and unbroken by joists or other projections. Ideally walls and ceiling should be fully insulated as this cuts down condensation, and the ceiling can then be finished with a hard gloss non-flaking paint. If not insulated, the ceiling may be finished in an absorbent plaster and painted with distemper. Where there is much steam, roof canopies are required to draw the steam up and prevent it drifting through the factory. Floors should be made of impervious, non-slip material. There must be an ample supply of water and hoses, and adequate drainage. The whole building must be well lit, properly heated and efficiently ventilated.

As regards equipment this should be so designed that it is easily cleaned, and stays clean while in use, with the least possible splashing of food particles, oil or water. All working surfaces should be smooth and impervious and all joinings watertight. There must be no chinks where dust and debris can collect. Metal, tiling or plastic should be used for all working surfaces, except

136

chopping-blocks. For these, there is still no good substitute for wood, but the surface must be kept clean by frequent scrubbing with wire brushes and detergents, and when worn and cracked it must be planed smooth again.

Wash-basins must be provided where the work is going on. They must be used frequently and properly, and they will not be used if they are sited far from the work-bench, in another part of the factory, or only in the toilets. There must be an adequate supply of hot and cold water, preferably with a mixer valve, liquid soap dispensers that work well and are kept topped up, paper towels that tear off cleanly, and foot-operated bins that open and shut properly. There must be attractive rest rooms and canteens.

All the foregoing means that a food factory should be an attractive place to enter and a pleasant place to work in, but everyone must be aware of the danger from germs. Nothing in the factory or on the part of the workers must add to this danger. Germs will get on the working surfaces, the floors, the walls, or the hands of the workers. They must be removed by washing and disinfection. This must be part of the instinctive routine of the factory, for germs give no sign of their presence.

The processes carried out in a food factory have already been described in Chapter 7. They consist mainly of preparing and cooking food. There is one exception—sausages. These are not cooked in the factory, and if there are germs on the surface of the meat when it reaches the factory, they will be in the centre of the sausages when they leave it. Their fate thereafter depends on how thoroughly they are fried (p. 58). Pies and roasts are usually sterile after cooking, but the danger is that germs present on raw meat find their way on to the cooked food, or that germs on the hands of workers in the factory may be added after cooking. This is especially liable to occur when glazes or jelly are added to meat or pies (p. 208), but it can happen in such simple processes as slicing or packing. Hygiene after cooking is even more important than hygiene before cooking, for much of the cooked food that leaves the factory will be eaten cold, and any added germs will still be alive.

The factory autoclave

In a hospital autoclave or disinfector there is a dirty and a clean side, completely separated by a solid wall and with no communicating doors. Dirty linen cannot get through to the clean side except through the autoclave which sterilizes it. The worker on the dirty side cannot get through at all. The same rigid precautions should apply in the food factory. Raw meat is the dirty linen, and cooked food is the sterile. The factory should be so designed that there is no connection at all between the two, and cooked foods should go out from the clean end of the factory to the shop and consumers, as free from contamination as the sterile linen goes from the autoclave to the wards and operating theatres. This is perhaps not wholly practicable, but there is no excuse for unintelligent design. We once saw a magnificent combined oven and refrigerator for cooking and cooling pies. It cost many thousands of pounds and its design was perfect, but it stood in the middle of the factory floor. Meat from the abattoir was wheeled in through the ever-open factory door. It was chopped and minced and finally conveyed with the dough cases to one end of the oven. From the other end a conveyor belt took the cool, cooked pies to be machine-wrapped in Cellophane, untouched by human hand: but on that journey they were exposed to the air which blew from the factory door across the chopping-tables and the mincing machines and which could gather thousands of germs from the raw abattoir meat on its way. There was no reasons at all why that superb oven should not have been built into a wall like the hospital autoclave. After all, an oven is really an autoclave. No one thought of it, because no one was aware of the danger. How often that word 'aware' comes into food hygiene!

As students of food hygiene we are not primarily concerned with details of structure and equipment. That is the function of the engineer and the designer, but they ought to know about food hygiene when they design their machines. Our concern is to be aware of the danger and to spread this awareness to all who work with food. This is not always easy. We once took photographs

138

inside a food factory. There were glaring errors in the hygiene of the place, but the sad thing was that the manager gave permission freely to photograph anything and everything, and was quite unaware that we were photographing examples of bad, not good hygienic conditions.

Canning

Canning is really a process of rapid cooking and sterilizing of food, and something has already been said about it in Chapter 7 (p. 62). Other methods of food preservation, for example drying or refrigeration, aim at preventing germs from multiplying (Chapter 21). The aim of canning is to kill any germs in the food, and then to seal the sterile food so securely that no new germs can get into it while it is stored.

Acid and non-acid foods

All canning processes depend on heat. The amount of heat depends on the kind of germ that has to be killed. Most heat-resistant disease germs, especially the germ of botulism (p. 46), cannot grow in highly acid food. Cans of acid foods need therefore only be heated to boiling-point, 100° C. (212° F.), for this temperature will destroy all the other disease germs which might grow in acid conditions. This applies to cans of fruit, tomatoes, rhubarb, and similar foods, where the acidity is high and the pH (acid factor) less than 3·7. In less acid food (pH over 3·7) spore-bearing germs like *Clostridium botulinum* can grow, and some of them survive boiling for hours on end. Cans of such food must be heated under steam pressure to a temperature of 121° C. (250° F.): a few minutes at this temperature kills all disease germs. This applies to cans of meat, fish, soups, vegetables, puddings and milk products.

Cooling and leakage

When the cans have been heated for the correct time and at the correct temperature in the autoclave, the steam is released and cold water is run into the autoclave. This is to make sure cans cool rapidly. There are three reasons for this: (1) to prevent the food from being over-cooked, (2) to prevent heat-loving (thermophilic) germs from multiplying during slow cooling, and (3) to avoid long hold-ups in the factory. (Thermophilic germs are not easily killed by heat: they multiply in warm food and spoil it, though they do not cause food poisoning.) Rapid cooling of the cans causes rapid changes of pressure. When the cans are very hot, the pressure inside, due to steam and hot air, may be as high as 20 lb. per square inch: the steam in the autoclave exerts a pressure almost equal to this, but when the autoclave pressure is released at the end of sterilization there is a much higher pressure inside the can than outside it, and this may push on any weak part of the can and cause a microscopic leak. As the can cools, a vacuum develops inside it, and this negative pressure pulls the weak part back again and closes the micro-leak, but as it does so it may suck in a minute drop of water, perhaps only 1/500th of 1 millilitre or less. If the water is pure, this does not matter. If it contains disease germs, they may multiply in the food with disastrous consequences (p. 198). There are two obvious ways of avoiding this: one is to use only pure water for cooling, chlorinated if required; the other is to introduce compressed air into the autoclave when the steam is released and so prevent the violent differences in pressure.

Handling and labelling

When the cans leave the autoclave, they go along conveyor belts to be labelled and packed. This may cause a good deal of bumping and battering, and this may cause a tiny leak on the seam of a can. If the can, the conveyor belt and all the other apparatus are dry and clean this may not matter, for germs do very poorly on clean, dry metal, but if the cans are wet, germs may easily slip through the leaking seam. It is very important that the hands of workers handling the cans at this stage are clean, dry and free from sores, as otherwise germs could pass from hands to cans and might get inside.

The whole canning process is a highly complicated one, and much research has been carried out to make it the safest of all forms of food-preservation. It is not completely proof against micro-leakage. This means that the highest standard of hygiene is required in the canning plant. When this is achieved, the micro-leak may not matter. Over 6,000 million cans of food are opened every year in Britain: the average number of outbreaks of food poisoning from canned food is 14 in a year.

18

Food Hygiene: Shops

Always have an eye to the mayne,
Whatsoever thou art chaunced to buy.

Lyly.

The modern food shop is a glorious piece of twentieth-century make-believe. Everything *looks* good. Pies are perfect, cream cakes catch the customer's eye, roast chickens make innocent mouths water, hams and tongues torture hungry gastric juices, and as the shopkeeper lifts a joint lovingly in his hands, breathing over it almost with affection, nothing can seem more appetizing and wholesome or further removed from anything that could possibly do one harm. It is all so attractive and fits in so well with twentieth-century sophistication that the modern shopper accepts it as an impeccable part of the luxury of living. Yet the cream in the cakes came from the udder of a cow which might have been diseased, the ham came from the hind leg of a pig that spent its life in a sty and ended it on an abattoir floor, the chicken came from an intensive flock that might have been alive with germs, and the butcher's joint of meat reached him only after a long and dangerous journey from the stock farm to his back shop. There are plenty of hazards in the modern food industry. The shopper should 'always have an eye to the mayne'.

The Butcher's Shop

The butcher's raw material is meat. Most of it is good, wholesome meat, but some of it some time is bound to be contaminated with food-poisoning germs. His equipment and his technique should be knowingly planned to prevent germs spreading in his shop. The important word is 'knowingly', for many, perhaps most butchers do not know about germs on meat.

The chopping-block

One of the butcher's main jobs is to chop and cut meat into suitable joints and portions—a skilled job, but also one which involves a lot of handling. The chopping-block is made of wood—there is no other material that can take the blow of the chopper without ruining the blade or jarring the butcher's arm. However the chopper as it sinks into the block can take meat and germs with it, and in the chinks and crevices the germs can multiply enormously. The block must be cleaned regularly and scrupulously (p. 137), and no cooked meat should ever be placed on or near it. The chopper and the butcher's hands also become covered with germs: they must be washed thoroughly and frequently (see below).

Sausages and mince

The butcher may sell sausages straight from the factory and over these he has little bacteriological control: he may contaminate the outside of the skins with his hands but those surface germs will be killed in the frying-pan. Often he makes his own sausages. First he minces the meat, and if there are germs on its surface he distributes them thoroughly through the mince. Then he packs the minced meat into a sausage machine which forces it out into sausage skins. The butcher cannot be blamed if surface germs are now in the middle of the sausages, but he can be blamed if he does not thoroughly cleanse the mincing and sausage machine before the next batch is made. The practice of pounding sausage meat into the machine with bare fist is inexcusable—there may be salmonellae on the fist from meat already handled, or *Clostridium welchii* or staphylococci from his own body.

Mince is a safer food than sausages, for it is always more thoroughly cooked and the crumbs of meat, instead of being packed in a skin, are all exposed to equal heat. Of course, not every sausage contains food-poisoning germs, and thorough cooking or frying kills any germs that do get in.

The counter

Germs on raw meat on a butcher's counter are bound to contaminate the counter. Any other meat placed on the counter will pick up some of these germs. Knives used for cutting the meat, scales used for weighing it, and the butcher's hands that carry it, must all become contaminated. It is impossible to visualize the spread of infection across the counter, for germs are invisible, but if swabs are rubbed on the counter, the scales, the knives, the joints of meat and the butcher's hands, and then stroked across plates of jelly in the laboratory, the colonies of germs that grow overnight will be easily seen by the naked eye in the morning. There will be many thousands of colonies, each composed of thousands of germs, and these may all have been derived from one piece of meat placed on the counter the morning before. Once on the move, germs can cover a surface quickly, but they always depend on help from some human. If this help is denied them, their life is short.

A butcher's counter should be made of impermeable material—plastic, metal, marble or tiling is suitable. Wood should not be tolerated, except for the chopping-block. The counter should be washed several times during the day with hot water containing detergent and disinfectant. The water should be drawn fresh from the hot-water supply each time; buckets of water kept under the counter all day become dangerously contaminated with germs. A fresh cloth or brush should be used each time and not used again till sterilized by boiling. There should be a wash-hand basin in the shop with a supply of hot and cold water, a liquid soap dispenser and a roll of paper towels. The practice of rinsing the hands in a bucket of water and drying them on the same cloth or towel all day should not be tolerated. 'Can the small family butcher afford all this?' We can almost hear the question being asked, but is it demanding very much that a shopkeeper selling food should keep his shop and his person clean?

A butcher often sells canned meats, pies, brawns and other ready-cooked meat products. If he does, it is essential that the raw

144

and cooked foods be kept separate. The same knife or cutting machine should never be used for raw and cooked meat, unless they are sterilized in between. The same balance should not be used, nor should the butcher handle cooked after raw meat without first thoroughly washing his hands. Ideally cooked meats and raw meats should be served from different counters and by different staff. This may all sound idealistic and extreme, but germs on raw meat are one thing: they will be killed in cooking. Germs on cooked meat are quite different: they will multiply on the cooked food and then go straight into the customer's mouths. In the Aberdeen typhoid outbreak of 1964, over 500 people got typhoid fever, but it all arose from one opened tin of corned beef, the germs in which spread in the shop to many other pieces of cooked meat (p. 199).

The display cabinet or window

The butcher must display his wares, and he does so either in a display cabinet or in the shop window. The main danger of this practice is that on a hot day such cabinets or windows can become almost incubators and any germs present on the meat are encouraged to multiply. The only way round this is to use refrigerated display cabinets, or to display as little food as possible and keep reserve stocks in a chilled room or refrigerator. Pies and cooked meats should not be displayed alongside raw meat: they are better not displayed at all, unless in separate refrigerated cabinets. All display cabinets and window slabs must be kept thoroughly clean.

The back shop

It must be remembered that a refrigerator does not kill germs. It stops them multiplying, but if there are germs on a piece of meat put in a refrigerator at night, they will still be there in the morning and they will start multiplying again if the meat is put in the warm shop window. It must also be emphasized that a butcher's back shop is just as important as, if not more important than the front shop. The customer does not see the back shop: the food hygienist should.

The Baker's Shop

The baker's differs from the butcher's shop in several respects as regards the risk of food poisoning. The main difference is that nearly all the baker offers for sale is already cooked. This is both an advantage and a disadvantage: an advantage in that if the cooking has been thorough, any germs in the constituents will have been killed: a disadvantage in that if germs have survived light cooking, or been added after cooking, they will multiply on the food in the shop and in the customer's home before being eaten. Another difference is that many of the baker's products are dry: bread is too dry for food poisoning germs to grow in it, as are pastries, sponges and biscuits. If cream, jam or other filling is added, however, the sponge or pastry above and below become moistened, and germs can then multiply in comfort. Pies are often made and sold in the baker's shop and they contain enough moisture to allow any germs in their centre to grow rapidly, given the correct temperature. Eggs are greatly used by bakers and bring danger of contamination (p. 101). Cream, both dairy and artificial, is lavishly used and forms an ideal medium for the growth of germs (p. 105). The bakery workers themselves may be carriers of germs, and they can very easily contaminate baked goods by handling them, especially when adding jams or cream fillings.

The bakery or back shop

A bakery can be a very dusty place, with flour and egg and other powdery dust on the floor, on tables and ledges, on clothes and hands, and suspended in the air. Such dust is inevitable during baking, but if it contains germs it may settle on food and contaminate it. As far as possible, then, there should be a dirty and clean room in a bakery (p. 152), and baked goods should be stored in the clean room till moved into the shop. Obviously everything should be done to keep down the dust. Floors should be made of smooth, impermeable material that can be easily cleaned, and tables and all working benches should have metal or plastic tops, not wood which offers chinks and cracks for the dust to settle into. Good ventilation is required.

There must be adequate facilities for cleaning and sterilizing equipment. Most artificial cream and liquid egg is now delivered sterile to bakeries, but if any batch is not, then mixing bowls and other equipment contaminated with it can pass the infection on to other mixes. It is, therefore, essential that all such equipment be sterilized after every use, and it is much safer to throw away any mix not used, than to attempt to keep it till the next day. Table tops and other surfaces should be washed thoroughly several times a day. There must be wash-basins, liquid soap containers, and paper towels conveniently sited for all workers: they should wash frequently during baking operations.

Fig. 14. The front shop may appear attractive, but its safety depends on conditions in the back shop

The front shop

When the cakes and other baked foods come into the front shop, they must be protected from contamination. All the goods should be covered, either in display counters and cabinets or under individual covers. They should be handled henceforth by no one, staff

147

or customers, and they should be protected from germs that may be sprayed as fine droplets from the nose or mouth. Many of the cakes and sponges are excellent culture media for staphylococci, and in the course of a day several carriers of staphylococci are likely to enter the shop. There should be no fingering or touching whatever, and always glass between cake and customer. Cake tongs should be used by staff when serving.

None of this, of course, will do anything to prevent food poisoning if germs are already in the food when it comes from the back shop. The problem of window display enters here again. In a warm window a few germs in a few hours can increase to thousands, and the thousands soon to millions. One must compromise between complete safety and the need to display goods. A window may be very attractive, but its safety depends mainly on conditions in the back shop.

19

Food Hygiene: The Kitchen

Tis an ill cook that cannot licke his own fingers.
Shakespeare. *Romeo and Juliet*, IV, ii

It is difficult to improve on Shakespeare, as far as language goes: and the art of the kitchen obviously fascinated him—'the kneading: the making of the cake, the heating of the oven, and the baking: nay you must stay the cooling too'. However he was not a food hygienist, and we can have no licking of fingers in the modern kitchen. Better perhaps the warning from the Old Testament, 'There is death in the pot', or Garrick's, 'Heaven sends us good meat, but the Devil sends cooks.' Dickens, too, can be of help: 'C-l-e-a-n, clean, verb active, to make bright, to scour.'

In the kitchen we have come to the end of the infection trail. There have been many hazards on the way. Here in the kitchen, food may be rendered safe, or made more poisonous. The dangers to which food is exposed in the kitchen have been described in Chapter 8, and need only be summarized here. There may be germs on the raw food coming in, and these can be transferred to the cooked food going out. The staff may add germs to the food, from their fingers, their noses or their intestines. There may be germs on the floors, on the tables and in the air, and these can settle on the food. Cooking temperatures may be too low and the time too short, and then the partially cooked food can take a long time cooling—conditions much appreciated by food-poisoning organisms. Perhaps there is not enough refrigerator or cold-room space, and germs still alive at the end of the day can multiply overnight while enjoying gentle warmth in the dark. Any or all of these hazards affect safety. How they are dealt with determines whether the food going forward to the table is sound and wholesome, or poisonous and unfit for human consumption. *Unfortunately it must usually be consumed before it is known to be unfit.*

Education

We must now consider what can be done to make kitchens safe. By far the most important thing is the education of the staff. If the chef or catering officer understands the mechanism of food infection, he can prevent it in his kitchen, even if it is not of the most modern design or furnished with the latest equipment. He must examine in detail every process that takes place, from the receiving of the raw materials till the finished product is on the table and, even later, till the meal is cleared away, the waste disposed of, the left-overs safely dealt with and the last dish or knife and fork thoroughly washed and put away. He must examine all these processes critically, and if he has any doubts he should ask someone better informed to go round with him—a public health inspector, a bacteriologist, a medical officer. It does not matter who, provided it is someone who has studied and understands the detailed hazards that underlie the preparation and distribution of food. Again and again, and at every point, they will find that it is people who count. The staff must know what they are doing and why they are doing it. If they don't understand a process they can ruin it, as the kitchen worker does who collects the plates from an efficient dish-washing machine and wipes them with a contaminated cloth (see p. 155).

Kitchen design

The food hygienist is not an architect, but he or she should be able to advise on the principles that must underlie hygienic kitchen design. They are simple. Germs can lurk in the dust on floors, on tables and working surfaces, and in the air. They may be present on walls and window-sills, even on ceilings; as long as they stay there, they do no harm, but if they drop off in condensation water they can fall on food. Walls must therefore be of impermeable washable material, and insulated to cut down condensation:

ceilings likewise, or if this is not possible, then finished in absorbent plaster. Ventilation must be efficient to suck out vapour and dust. The floor must be of non-absorbent finish, non-skid, even, and easily cleaned. Table tops and working surfaces must be of metal, plastic or any other non-absorbent, non-splintering material. There must be no cracks or chinks in the hygienic kitchen. All this adds up to one principle of kitchen design, that dust and fine debris must find no secure lodgement anywhere in the kitchen.

A second principle is that there must be plenty of space, and the space must be functionally designed and arranged. In the reception area one needs enough room to be able to receive separately different types of foodstuffs: potatoes and other vegetables that may have earth still on them carrying *Clostridium welchii*, raw meat that may be contaminated with salmonellae, and cooked food such as hams and pies that should be free of germs and should remain so in the kitchen. The hams and pies should go straight to cold storage and should not make contact with the other foods till these have come separately through the kitchen and are cooked and ready to go to the dining table. In the preparation area also, there must be division of space and labour. Vegetables must be cleaned and prepared separately from raw meat and, if cans of food are being opened, this food must be handled well away from the raw food area, and kept away from it. This all seems simple and obvious, but neglect of this principle is one of the commonest errors in kitchen practice.

The cooking area must be well organized so that every process can be supervised. The chef or catering officer must be able to check quickly that correct temperatures and correct times are being maintained. When the food is cooked it must be taken to an area that has not been used for the preparation of raw food, and workers on the preparation side should not cross to the cooked food area. If the food is to be eaten hot, then it must be kept hot, above 65° C. (131° F.), so that germs cannot grow in it; it should not be allowed to go tepid, around 45°–50° C. (113°–122° F.), when germs will multiply rapidly in it: and, as far as possible, it should go forward to the table at once, and not lie in the kitchen for hours. If, however, the food is to be eaten cold, for example cakes or creams or cold meats, then it should be taken to a cooling area well away from preparation and cooking areas so that dust and debris cannot float over from the raw to the cooked food. This is an especial danger in bakeries where contaminated dust is an obvious risk, but the danger exists in any kitchen. Food-poisoning germs, remember, are invisible. A second reason for separation is that kitchens are warm places, and cooked food will cool very slowly there, and any germs that get on it will be encouraged to multiply and produce toxin.

Finally there must be plenty of cold storage space to avoid any hold-up in the flow of food through the kitchen. This cold storage should be structurally separated from the kitchen to prevent dust or contaminated air flowing from one to the other. The cold storage area for cooked food must, of course, be entirely separate from the chilling room used for the reception and storage of meat and other raw foods.

The foregoing may all sound idealistic. We can only comment that in the production, preparation, cooking and distribution of our food there is ample room for idealism.

Washing up

Dish washing or washing up is a routine practice in most kitchens. There is no good reason why it should be. No surgeon would tolerate the washing and cleaning of instruments and towels in the middle of the operating theatre, and no chefs should be required to have dirty dishes washed where he operates. Washing-up sinks and machines should be outside the kitchen.

The effect of heat. The aim of washing up is to remove all food particles from dishes, crockery and cutlery, and to kill any germs that may be on them. Two agents are available for this purpose, heat and chemicals. Heat acts by melting fat and grease and so helping to remove food debris: it also kills germs by direct action if it is hot enough. The hottest most hands can bear is around 50° C. (122° F.). This is not hot enough to destroy germs, and if

152

dishes are washed at this temperature, germs can still be grown from them afterwards. Usually these are not disease germs, and in any case their presence on plates and cutlery, though highly undesirable, is not a very great danger, for the germs will not multiply on dry dishes. On mixing bowls and similar utensils by contrast, the presence of germs is very dangerous, for when the bowl is next used the germs will be able to enter the mixture and multiply if given suitable temperature and time. Clearly one-sink washing is not satisfactory for such utensils. If a second sink is available, the dishes can be rinsed in this in water at a higher temperature, say 80° C. (176° F.), and this will destroy disease germs. Failing this, a disinfectant or bactericidal substance can be added to the washing water (see below). In a dish-washing machine, where hands play no part, water at higher temperature can be used, 60° C. (140° F.) for the wash and 80° C. (176° F.) for the rinse.

Soap, detergents and disinfectants. Chemicals are, in fact, always added to washing water, usually one or other of many available detergents. The best-known detergent is soap, though it is usually not regarded as a detergent at all. It belongs to the anionic group of detergents and is the sodium or potassium salt of fatty acids. When any salt is added to water it dissociates into its ions: sodium chloride, common salt, separates into sodium and chloride ions; the sodium is the cation and the chloride the anion: the anion is positively, the cation negatively charged. Some detergents owe their action to their positively charged anions, and are called anionic detergents, some to negatively charged cations, the cationic detergents. A few have no electrical charge at all and are non-ionic. The only practical point in knowing this is that anionic detergents can be used along with soap, but the cationic detergents cannot. On the other hand some cationic detergents have bactericidal or disinfectant action as well as their detergent action. The anionic detergents usually have not, though soap has, but they can have a disinfectant added to them. Hypochlorite, a form of bleach, is often so added. It is usually very difficult, or even impossible, to discover what any commercial detergent consists of, and one must rely on the makers' instructions regarding their use.

A detergent is a substance which removes dirt and grease by forming a suspension or an emulsion carrying off the dirt in it. The first step is to wet the surface. If water is dropped on top of wax or grease it forms globules, but if a wetting agent is added it forms a fine film. Commercial detergents all have wetting agents in their formula. Usually they include also a water-softening agent which may be something as familiar as washing soda. They may also have a foaming agent added. Foaming is not a necessary part of the cleansing process: it looks effective in the sink, and perhaps on the TV screen, but it can be a nuisance in the washing machine. Soap is a very good anionic detergent in soft water. In hard water it brings out the calcium and magnesium, which cause the hardness, and these form a scum on the water which is difficult to get rid of. The water-softening additive in commercial detergents keeps the calcium and magnesium in solution and avoids the scum: this is their main advantage over soap, but there is nothing magic about them.

The bactericidal, or germ-killing action of hot water is aided by the use of detergents and increased by the use of disinfectants: just as the action of both detergents and disinfectants is increased by heat. A combination of all three is therefore the ideal. In the one-sink method, where dishes are washed by hand, disinfectant is certainly required in addition to detergent. In the two-sink method or in dish-washing machines the temperatures can be so high that detergent only is required, though disinfectant in addition does no harm. It is not possible to give rules about the amount of detergent or disinfectant to add, for the many commercial products differ widely in their formulae. It is important to follow the makers' instructions and it is essential to ensure that the required temperature and the correct concentration of chemicals are maintained *throughout* the washing process. Temperatures can fall if machines or sinks are not supervised, and chemicals are used up by contact with grease and food debris, and the solution then needs topping up. Both temperature and concentrations are controlled automatically in modern equipment, but only if the equipment is serviced and inspected regularly. Failure to check washing-up processes, either by hand or machine, can lead to unsatisfactory and perhaps dangerous bacteriological conditions after the wash.

Cloths and brushes. A wet dish-cloth is an unpleasant object. Sodden with suds, swollen with grease and speckled with food particles it is very lacking in aesthetic appeal. There is no corresponding lack of bacterial content, for often such a cloth is teeming with germs. Bacteriologists have taken snips of wet dish-cloths, rubbed them over culture plates and then grown millions of germs from them in the laboratory. These are usually not disease germs, but staphylococci and salmonellae have been grown. In any case, it cannot be regarded as good hygiene to wipe dishes with wet

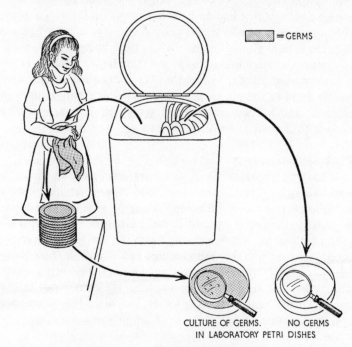

= GERMS

CULTURE OF GERMS.   NO GERMS
IN LABORATORY PETRI DISHES

FIG. 15. Dishes should be stacked and dried in air.
Drying cloths are often covered with germs

155

germ-laden cloths. Nylon brushes are much better, for these can be easily cleaned and sterilized. Dish-cloths can be boiled, but they make an unpleasant brew.

If dishes have been washed or rinsed in really hot water, they will dry in air, and this is the best way to dry them, provided they can be stacked so that water runs *off* them and does not collect in cold pools *on* them. If they cannot be so stacked—lack of space is the usual problem—then they may be dried with sterile cloths. The difficulty is to keep the cloth sterile. Germs will not grow readily on a dry cloth, but the cloth does not remain dry for long, and unless the drying cloth is frequently changed, it too can become charged with germs. Drying sterile dishes with such a cloth undoes the sterilization. (It may be mentioned here that the practice of wiping a plate with a napkin before placing it in front of a diner, although meant to add to the grace of dining, is not blameless from the food hygienist's point of view. Bacteriologists have made cultures from such napkins and found them far from sterile. It is a foolish convention of the restaurant.) If dishes after washing cannot be dried in the air, disposable paper towels can be used in place of cloths. They are virtually germ free, but the difficulty often is to dispose of the disposables.

The hospital laboratory

A hospital laboratory is quite a hazardous place in which to work. There are germs everywhere, many of them very dangerous, but laboratory workers are acutely aware of what they are handling, and on the alert constantly to make sure germs do not spread.

The outlook in a kitchen should be exactly the same. There are germs there too, and they must be kept under control. *There is one big difference.* If anything goes wrong, it is not the kitchen workers who suffer. The results of their mistakes are carried out of the kitchen to the buffet or dining tables. The diner has no defence against a careless chef.

20

The Food Handler

This is the most important chapter in the book. It may also be the most boring, for it is full of rules, and rules can be deadening things. If one understands the reasons behind rules, they can come to life and be exciting. Behind the rules of food hygiene there is an exciting story, the life history of countless millions of living unicellular germs striving to establish themselves, often very successfully, in the bodies of multicellular animals and man. If we constantly remain aware of this struggle, then our food hygiene rules cease to be lifeless, but can be seen instead as tactics in a form of bacteriological warfare. Awareness is all.

Person

The food handler should be a clean person. This may seem too obvious to state, yet some cases of food poisoning have been caused simply because the food handler was not clean. The food handler should try not to handle food. When he must, he should do so with hands as clean as possible. How does he keep them clean?

Hands. Germs love cracks and crevices, on tables, floors and benches, but also on hands. So the food handler must keep his or her hands as smooth and soft as possible, and there are many excellent lotions and barrier creams which he can use several times a day, perhaps when going off duty for meals or rest periods. Very hot water, if it contains alkali and detergents, can lead to roughness or sogginess of the skin, especially in the nail folds, and it is wise to wear gloves when one has to immerse the hands for long periods in such water. In general, however, gloves are not advisable, because they can make the hands sweat, and hot, moist hands invite germs to multiply.

157

FIG. 16. Food handlers can be dangerous people

Washing must be thorough and frequent. The food handler should instinctively wash his hands before touching food, and always after handling raw meat or vegetables. A dispenser of liquid soap is much more hygienic than a cake of soap, for the latter always has a scum on it, and a pool of turbid water under it, and germs can grow in this. A disinfectant such as hexachlorophane can be added to the liquid soap, and thus help to keep down the number of germs on hands. The dispenser itself must be kept clean, and no clot should be allowed to form on the nozzle. Nail-brushes are best made of nylon brushes for they can be washed and cleaned more easily than hair brushes. They should not be kept immersed in disinfectant fluid, for this often loses its disinfecting properties and becomes contaminated with live germs. The brushes should be changed several times a day. They can be washed in a disinfectant fluid, such as 3 per cent hexachlorophane, and dried thoroughly. Ideally heat-sterilized nail-brushes should be used: they should be available at least in every hospital kitchen. Nail-brushes can remove dirt only if the bristles can reach it, and food handlers ought therefore to keep their nails short. Food-poisoning germs have often been grown from under nails.

Two kinds of germs may be present on the hands, native germs and foreign germs. By native germs we mean germs which normally inhabit and multiply on the skin, often deep down in the pores. Staphylococci are the common native germs. Foreign germs are those that get on the skin accidentally. These may be salmonellae, shigellae or clostridia, in fact any of the food-poisoning germs. There is a very important difference. Foreign germs are not at home on the skin and washing will remove them. Staphylococci are very much at home, and no amount of washing will dislodge them all. In fact scrubbing with hot water may bring the deep staphylococci nearer the surface and make the hands just as dangerous as before. This is one reason why surgeons, after thoroughly 'scrubbing up' in the theatre, still put on sterile gloves before operating. It has even been shown that if a surgeon has a hot shower before operating, he may disperse more staphylococci into the theatre air than he does without a shower. To the food handler the moral is clear. Even though his hands are as clean as he can make them, there may still be staphylococci on them. This is why he should touch food with his hands as little as possible.

Towels, like dish-cloths (p. 155), rapidly become contaminated, and roller towels should never be used. The only satisfactory towel is a paper one, dropped into a foot-operated bin after use. There are many excellent paper towel dispensers on the market, and a good paper towel does dry the hands. Hot-air driers are very hygienic, but they take a long time to get the hands really dry, and busy workers cannot wait.

Hair. Staphylococci grow very well on a scurfy scalp, and dandruff can fall over food very easily. This is an unpleasant thought, but food hygienists must face unpleasant facts. Hair must be kept clean and tidy and washed regularly with an anti-dandruff shampoo—there are reliable brands on the market. Caps should be worn, but they should really cover the hair and not be merely frilly ornaments. The *gros bonnet* or 'big hat' of the chef, besides giving him an air of authority, does protect food from dandruff. Hair cream, too, keeps hair in place, and prevents anything falling out of it, and is a good thing if it stops the food handler from throwing his hair back with his hand.

Clothes. Clothes should be light, clean and tidy, and the white apron or coat should be changed at least once daily. Germs cannot jump off clothes on to food, but hands are constantly in contact with clothes and germs can be transferred from one to the other. Soiled clothes in a kitchen, shop or factory are a sign of general slovenliness, and indicate that food hygiene in the work-place is not of a high order.

Health

Food handlers should be aware that illness in themselves can lead to outbreaks of food poisoning. They should therefore report any illness, however mild, and someone with a knowledge of food hygiene should decide whether it is of importance or not. A food handler who has an attack of diarrhoea and vomiting should always be put off duty till cleared by a doctor. Anyone with a nasal discharge, especially if it is purulent, should be examined by a doctor, for germs in a chef's nose can lead to disaster in the dining-room (p. 212). Sticky eyes may be dangerous for germs are so easily transferred to the hands. Sores, cuts and cracks on the hands are especially important, for often staphylococci get into them and they may be food-poisoning staphylococci. Cuts and sores should always be carefully dressed, and a food handler with a sore should not handle cooked food. If he must, the sore should be covered with a waterproof dressing, but even this has its dangers for it often makes the sore soggy, slow to heal and more attractive to staphylococci. It is, of course, impracticable to put every food handler off duty who cuts his finger, but if the food handler is aware of the danger he can take special care.

Before food handlers are employed they should be questioned about their health, and if they have had any illness of an intestinal type, the doctor may decide to carry out special tests first. These tests, however, are not completely reliable. A person might pass a test one week, and fail it the next, for carriers tend to excrete germs intermittently. The doctor must decide on history as well as on laboratory tests.

Habits

A food handler should have clean habits, and these should be instinctive. He washes his hands before touching food, and after touching food, because he knows that he can pass skin germs on to food, and that he can acquire germs on his hands from raw food, and then transfer it to cooked food. He washes his hands very thoroughly after emptying his bowels, because he knows that germs in the faeces can get through toilet paper on to his hands and so on to food. He is careful about using handkerchiefs, because he knows that though a handkerchief straight from the laundry is sterile, it can be covered with millions of germs after he blows his nose into it. He may, therefore, prefer to use paper handkerchiefs while on duty. He does not smoke on duty, not only because this is forbidden by law, but because he knows it is a dirty habit. Cigarette ash is sterile and will not cause food poisoning if it falls into food, but the food handler can get germs on his hands from his mouth and lips. Moreover, if there is cigarette ash all over the kitchen there are probably all sorts of harmful dust and debris as well. It is a sign of bad hygiene.

The good food handler does not lick his fingers to pick up wrapping-paper, nor does he blow into paper bags to open them. When he slices cold meat, he lifts the slice with a clean knife on to a clean plate or wrapping-paper, not with his bare hands. He uses tongs for lifting cakes and pastries, but, he uses tongs in the back as well as in the front shop. He need not be constantly thinking about food poisoning, but he understands how the germs of food poisoning get around, and he instinctively does everything in his power to make sure he does not help them on their way.

Equipment

The conscientious food handler likes to work with the best equipment, but even if he has to make do with something less than the latest, he looks after it well. When he has used a bowl for mixing, he makes sure the bowl is properly washed and sterilized before it is used again. He will clean and sterilize his knives and choppers frequently during the day, and he will make certain that knives used for raw meat are not used for cutting cooked meat. He realizes that table tops can be dangerous pieces of equipment, and he will thoroughly scrub and dry them as often as they become soiled. He will never have raw and cooked food on the same table; if possible not in the same room. He knows that slicing machines, liquidizers, mincers and other stainless-steel machines, though they may be bright and gleaming, can easily be contaminated with germs and he will arrange that these machines are dismantled frequently and thoroughly cleaned, if possible at least once a day. The food handler who knows his job takes nothing on trust.

Welfare

The food handler is entitled to good conditions. His working place should be bright, spacious and cheerful, and there should also be good welfare facilities behind it. Toilet facilities should be first-class, with modern water-closets with foot-operated flushes. There should be plenty of changing rooms with lockers for outdoor clothes and footwear. There must be an adequate number of wash-basins, properly equipped with soap dispensers and paper towels, and there should also be a supply of tissue-paper handkerchiefs. A rest room for off-duty periods should be clean and comfortable and the canteen should set the highest standard of hygiene. All this may sound very ideal and impracticable in the small shop, kitchen or factory, but only the ideal is good enough in food production. If the small establishment cannot reach an acceptable standard, it should be closed. Too many outbreaks have been caused by ignorance and filth.

Knowledge

Equipment, welfare, habits, health and hands—they are all important—but knowledge is more important still. Everyone who handles food should have some knowledge of food poisoning. A little learning may be a dangerous thing, if it is not digested and understood. Knowledge, on the other hand, implies an understanding of facts. The food hygienist and the food handler need all the knowledge they can acquire.

21

The Preservation of Food

*To get goods is the benefit of Fortune, to keepe them
the gift of Wisdome.*

Lyly

Raw food is never a sterile substance. Meat, flour, milk, sugar, anything and everything we eat—all are natural products, all part of the cycle of nature, all subject to corruption and decay. Much of the breaking-down processes are accomplished by germs, and these germs are on our food when we get it. They cause spoilage of food, and spoilage is simply the first stage in breaking complex into simple substances, and returning these simple substances into circulation in nature. These spoilage germs are carrying out an essential job, but from our point of view they are detrimental because, of course, they spoil our food. It becomes sticky or slimy or develops an off flavour. In other words, it goes bad.

With one or two exceptions we do not eat bad food. The exceptions are mainly game dishes in European kitchens, though strange fish dishes are eaten in other parts of the world (p. 120). We usually refer to our game as being 'high', not 'bad'. 'High' is a gastronomic term, 'bad' a food hygienist's term, but they both mean the same thing.

Spoilage germs

Spoilage of food is an economic, not a medical problem, for it is not bad food which causes food poisoning, but food which appears sound. The germs which cause food poisoning are quite distinct from spoilage germs. These latter lead different lives. They are on the whole hardier than food-poisoning germs, for they have a job to do and must be able to get on with it in adverse conditions. They can often withstand heat that kills food-poisoning germs, and they sometimes multiply at low temperatures at which other germs cannot grow. The food hygienist is concerned with both groups of germs. He must always remember that though he may kill or subdue the one by methods of food preservation, the other can survive many of his strategies and, unless controlled, can undo all his efforts.

The most obvious example is the pasteurization of milk. The temperature and time are adjusted to kill all the pathogenic germs likely to be found in milk: but these will not kill thermophilic or heat-loving germs. If the pasteurized milk were allowed to cool slowly, these germs would multiply rapidly as the milk passed through their favourite temperature range, and quickly spoil the milk. This is why the Regulations require that milk must be quickly cooled after pasteurization. There may also be in milk some germs which can grow in the cold and they may grow even when the milk is kept in a refrigerator. This explains why pasteurized milk does not keep indefinitely, for these cold-growing germs give an unpleasant taste to the milk though they do not sour it.

In this chapter the term preservation is used to cover all methods of keeping food, including sterilization as well as pasteurization, curing and radiation. Much of the information has already been given in earlier chapters but is brought together here for convenience.

Refrigeration and Chilling

The purpose of a domestic refrigerator is to stop germs from multiplying on food. The germs are not killed, and will start to grow again when the food is taken out into a warm room. The temperatures below which food-poisoning germs stop multiplying are:

Salmonellae	5° C. (41° F.)
Staphylococci	10° C. (52° F.)
Clostridium welchii	6·5° C. (43·7° F.)
Clostridium botulinum	5° C. (41° F.)

All these are well above freezing-point, so that there is no need to have the refrigerator at freezing-point, and a good deal of gas and electricity is wasted trying to keep the refrigerator at zero. A temperature of 5° C. (41° F.) is obviously low enough, though to be on the safe side one can aim at 3°–4° C. (37·4°–39·2° F.).

Some spoilage germs can still grow at these low temperatures, though slowly, and so food cannot be kept indefinitely in a refrigerator. A lot depends on the nature of the food and the degree of contamination when the food is placed in the refrigerator, but one week is probably the longest that food should be left in a refrigerator, and four to five days is safer.

REFRIGERATION
DOES NOT KILL GERMS

THEY ARE STILL ALIVE TO MULTIPLY
AT ROOM TEMPERATURE

Fig. 17

The use of a refrigerator

A refrigerator must be used with care and intelligence. It is meant for keeping food cold, not for cooling hot food. If hot food is placed in a refrigerator, the temperature is bound to rise and

166

this may encourage the growth of spoilage or even food-poisoning germs. Moreover, hot food, in cooling, gives off water vapour and this can condense on other foods and in this way, too, favour the growth of spoilage germs. A refrigerator must not be packed with food, for this prevents the circulation of cold air and leads to pockets of stagnant, warmer air. Bad ventilation and dampness inside a refrigerator are signs of unintelligent use. They are also conditions that encourage the growth of moulds and yeasts.

Defrosting must be carried out regularly, for the mechanism cannot work properly if the cooling coils are covered with a thick layer of ice. The inside of a refrigerator must be kept clean: it is good practice to wash the walls and trays during defrosting, making sure the interior is thoroughly dry before switching on again. Some moulds and yeasts grow even on the cold bare walls of a refrigerator; washing helps to get rid of them.

The cold room

A cold room is really a large refrigerator. It is, however, often used for cooling joints and other foods, and because of its size, there is not the same objection to this as in a refrigerator. Because of the increased moisture, ventilation becomes very important and a fan is advisable to keep air moving and prevent pools of dank, still air. Large institutions and factories often have special cooling rooms in which the hot food is exposed to a continuous current of cold air, and rapid cooling is achieved before the food is placed in the cold room or refrigerator.

Food kept in a refrigerator or cold room is chilled, not frozen. Microbial life is slowed down, but the food itself is not changed in any way, and its length of life is limited. A refrigerator is of great value in the temporary preservation of food, but its limitations must be understood.

Deep-freezing

A deep-freezer is a refrigerator for keeping food in the frozen state; all the fluid in the food, be it a pie, a trifle or a carcass, is changed to ice. In a domestic deep-freezer, the freezing and the

167

storing are carried out in the same refrigerator, but in a food factory or large institution the food is frozen before being put into the deep-freeze. This is most effectively done by blast freezing. The food is placed in a special chamber, the blast freezer, and subjected to a continuous blast of air at under $-20°$ C. ($-4°$ F.). The time and temperature are varied according to the type and texture of the food, but $\frac{1}{2}$ to $1\frac{1}{2}$ hours is an average time at a temperature between $-20°$ C. and $-40°$ C. ($-4°$ F. and $-40°$ F.). This rapid method does not affect the flavour or the texture of the food. Slower methods can affect both.

When the food is frozen, it is packed in the deep-freeze and kept at around $-18°$ C. ($0°$ F.). This, of course, is far below the temperature at which food-poisoning organisms stop multiplying, but freezing does not kill them, nor does it destroy any toxins present in the food before freezing. When the food is taken out of the deep-freeze and thawed, any food-poisoning germs in the food before freezing will start to multiply again, and unless the food is thoroughly cooked, food poisoning may follow (p. 193). If staphylococcal enterotoxin were present even thorough cooking would not destroy it.

Not all life comes to an end in the deep-freeze, for some bacteria, moulds and yeasts can multiply at this low temperature. This is especially the case if the freezing has not been thorough and somewhere in the frozen food there are pockets of unfrozen moisture, for moisture favours growth. Such growth of germs can lead to spoilage of the food, although serious spoilage is uncommon in efficient freezing plants.

More important than spoilage in the deep-freeze is loss of flavour; this seems to depend on a factor of time which varies for different foods, but there is very little loss till after 6 weeks. The reason for the loss of flavour is not known but it is probably due to some subtle chemical changes.

When food is taken out of the deep-freeze, it must be thawed thoroughly and cooked immediately. Thawing of a chicken or turkey takes between 8 and 12 hours. If thawing is incomplete, the heat of cooking may not penetrate the whole carcass, and any

168

germs still alive in the centre when cooking begins are still alive when the bird is 'done' (p. 195). Food taken out of the deep-freeze and thawed should never be refrozen, for germs may have multiplied during the unfreezing and the food may be badly contaminated when returned to the freezer.

Frozen meals

The tendency has been to think of deep-freezing as a method of preserving only fresh food, or a limited variety of cooked meat and fish. There is little doubt that the deep-freeze will be used more and more for cooked foods of all kinds on a commercial and institutional scale. Whole meals can be cooked and frozen, stored in the deep-freeze, and thawed, reheated and served on demand. If the period of storage is not too long, there is no loss of flavour and the food is as good as freshly cooked food. Research is still required into the mechanics of thawing and heat penetration, but with food carefully prepared and thoroughly cooked before being frozen there is far less risk of food poisoning than with raw deep-frozen food. The method has already been successfully tried in hospitals, and it is bound to spread to the home. Prejudice, of course, will have to be overcome. There are always those who claim that nothing can ever be so good as home-cooked food, as if every housewife was by natural endowment a cordon bleu cook. The same type of person objects to pasteurized milk because it has been subjected to moderate heat, though he will gladly drink a glass of piping hot milk as a night cap, because he is used to it. The emphasis in this book has been on food hygiene as a discipline for preventing food poisoning, but the food hygienist is concerned with all aspects of food production. He has little use for prejudices and must be ready at all times to examine critically the methods of conventional catering. Deep-frozen meals *will* become more common. The food hygienist must be alert to meet the changes.

Heat Treatment

Heat is the most effective weapon for destroying germs and so preserving food. If the thermal death point of a germ is known, then the application of heat above that temperature to the food, provided it penetrates the food, will destroy the germ. A temperature of 60° C. (140° F.) for 20 minutes will destroy salmonellae but it would not kill *Clostridium botulinum* or many of the thermophilic (heat-loving) spoilage germs. Complete sterilization of food can be achieved if sufficient heat is applied, but the taste and texture of the food may be changed in the process, and the changes may not be acceptable. Corned beef is cooked when sterilized in the can and that is how we like to eat it, but sterilized milk has a 'cooked' flavour which many people dislike. Some meats, such as hams and tongues, lose texture and substance if heated too much in the can and for them less intense heat is used in the canning industry (see below). Let us look at the main methods of preservation by heat.

Pasteurization

Pasteur was the great French biologist who did much of the pioneer work in the science of bacteriology. One of his early interests was in the fermentation of wine and beer. These sometimes go sour through the production of acetic acid by germs, and Pasteur found that by heating the bottled wine and beer to between 50° C. and 60° C. (122° F. and 140° F.) for a few minutes, souring was prevented. This discovery was a great boon to the wine trade and the process became known as 'pasteurization'. It was soon found that the same treatment applied to milk delayed its souring, and pasteurization of milk first became popular as a means of prolonging its keeping life. It was later discovered that by controlling the time and temperature of the process all the disease germs present in milk could be killed. This included the germ of tuberculosis, *Mycobacterium tuberculosis*, and, as a result of pasteurization, tuberculosis of the spine and bones, which had been a great scourge of childhood, almost ceased to exist. Pasteurization has for long been regarded as a heat process applied only to milk, but the term is now in use for other products such as liquid egg, ice-cream and some varieties of canned meats. It is also coming

170

into use for the treatment of food by radiation, where heat is not used at all: food can, in fact, be treated by radiation while still frozen (p. 176). Pasteurization is not sterilization, for it does not kill thermophilic (heat-loving) spoilage germs. As applied to milk, liquid egg and ice-cream, pasteurization does mean that the product is free of living disease germs. Applied to some canned foods, where penetration is not so easy as in milk, pasteurization may mean only that germs have been reduced to a safe level. Where disease germs are concerned no level is really safe, and such 'pasteurized' products require to be watched carefully by the food hygienist.

Milk, eggs and ice-cream. Pasteurization of milk may be achieved in one of two ways:

(a) Milk is heated to between 62·8° C. and 65·6° C. (145° F. to 150° F.) and held at that temperature for 30 minutes.

(b) Milk is heated at 71·7° C. (161° F.) for 15 seconds.

The milk must be immediately cooled to 10° C. (50° F.). Both these types of milk must be labelled 'Pasteurized Milk'. A third method is to heat milk at 132° C. (270° F.) for 1 second in an approved apparatus which diverts any milk which does not reach this temperature. Such milk must then be sealed in sterile containers and may then be sold as 'Ultra Heat Treated Milk'. A fourth method is to filter and homogenize milk and then heat it in sealed bottles to at least 100° C. (212° F.): the time required is controlled by laboratory tests. This milk is sold as 'Sterilized Milk'. All these grades of milk must be produced under conditions laid down by law and only under license. The conditions are defined in 'The Milk (Special Designation) Regulations, 1963' and 'The Milk (Special Designation) (Amendment) Regulations, 1965'. It should be noted that cream is not covered by the regulations and much contaminated cream still reaches the consumer (p. 105).

The temperatures and times for the pasteurization of liquid egg and ice-cream have already been given in Chapter 13 (pp 101 and 112). The conditions are defined in 'The Liquid Egg (Pasteurization) Regulations, 1963' and 'The Ice-Cream (Heat Treatment, etc.) Regulations, 1959'.

Pasteurized canned meats. Milk, liquid egg and ice-cream, pasteurized according to the regulations, are free of living disease germs. The same cannot be guaranteed for pasteurized canned hams and some other meats. Full sterilization heat treatment apparently causes shrinkage, loss of flavour and change of colour and texture in some meat products, and manufacturers wish to avoid this by subjecting these meats to a less severe heat treatment which is called in the trade 'pasteurization'. Many of these meats are also treated with salts so that they are partially cured (see below) and this helps to keep down the growth of germs, but failure of heat penetration is the difficulty in such compromise processes, and these 'pasteurized' hams and meats are not sterile and may even contain disease germs such as staphylococci or salmonellae. The heat and curing processes should ensure that these are present in small numbers only, but if only a few are present after pasteurization they can multiply inside the cans if the temperature suits them. All such canned meats must be regarded as perishable and they should be stored in the cold, and this should be stated on the label. They are not suitable for long storage.

Heat sterilization

Sterilization by heat requires the application of heat under pressure. The temperature usually achieved in the canning industry for this purpose is 121° C. (249° F.). The germ which it is essential to kill is *Clostridium botulinum*. The vegetative form of the germ is killed at 80° C. (176° F.) but the spores require exposure to 120° C. for 5 minutes. The toxins of *Clostridium botulinum* are all destroyed at temperatures well below 100° C. The process of sterilization by canning and the difficulties that may arise are discussed in Chapters 7 and 17 (pp. 62 and 139).

Drying, Curing and Smoking

Drying

Germs require moisture for multiplication. If the moisture content of food is reduced, germs cannot continue to live on it. This is

172

the principle underlying the preservation of food by drying, but it is important to realize that germs are not killed by drying, and that they will grow again when moisture is added. We have already seen that this is especially true of dried egg which has in the past caused many outbreaks of salmonella food poisoning.

The oldest method of drying was by exposing food to the sun. This is still used in some countries for drying fruit and fish. One can see acres of grapes drying in the sun in Greece near Corinth: the word currant, or dried grape, is probably a corruption of Corinth. In Scotland till quite recently fish was salted and dried in the sun, and, in Switzerland, Bindenfleisch is still prepared by drying the meat in the open air. In most commercial production, some form of artificial heat is used. In tunnel drying the food passes through a tunnel while exposed to a blast of hot air. In belt drying food is carried on conveyor belts through hot-air chambers. In spray drying liquid is forced into a chamber where it meets a blast of hot air and falls to the floor as a powder, and in roller drying liquid is sprayed on hot rollers and the dry film it forms is removed by scrapers. Spray and roller drying are both used for liquid egg or milk and the temperature may be less than $51.5°$ C. ($125°$ F.), well below the temperature required to kill food-poisoning germs. As long as dried food remains dry germs will not multiply in it, but the amount of contamination in the dried food depends on the amount in the food before drying.

The advantages of drying are that it is cheap, and storage is made easier because the bulk and weight of the food is reduced when the water is dried out of it. Disadvantages are that the flavour of the food is altered, the colour is changed due to oxidation and caramelization, and, when reconstituted with water, the final product is different in shape, colour and taste from the original food. Nevertheless, many dried foods are very acceptable, though different, and drying is likely to continue for long as a convenient method of food storage and preservation. Vacuum drying and freeze drying are newer methods in which the drying temperature is lower and there is less change in the food. Freeze drying is the only method which produces a sterile product.

173

Please note this last sentence should read:

A freeze dried product is one in which the water content is so low that germs cannot grow in it.

Curing

In curing, chemicals are added to the food to kill germs in it or stop them multiplying. Salt is the commonest chemical used. At a concentration of 18 per cent, strong brine, it will stop all multiplication and kill many germs by osmosis, and it is really a form of dehydration or drying as far as its effect on germs is concerned. Staphylococci are very tolerant of salt, and can grow at concentrations below 18 per cent, but most other food-poisoning germs are checked at 10 per cent or even lower. The vegetative forms of *Clostridium botulinum* are not checked at under 10 per cent, but the spores may be prevented from germinating at a salt concentration as low as 3·5 per cent, although this cannot be guaranteed. Nitrites are often added to the salt in a concentration around 100 parts per million and this seems to add to the preserving action, though the mode of action is not clear. This is the kind of curing given to some meats before 'pasteurization' in cans, and in some way the curing seems to make the pasteurizing more effective than could be explained simply by the temperature. There is a good deal more of tradition and custom than of strict science in curing, and for this reason the processes must be carefully watched, for when the exact mechanism of a process is not understood, slight changes in method can have unexpected results.

Acetic acid, or vinegar, is used in pickling foods and here the acidity of the food prevents the growth of food-poisoning germs: the pH, or acid index, of pickled food is usually as low as 3–3·5, and food-poisoning germs will not grow below 4·5. Spices are often added to pickled food but they probably have no curing action though they taste as if they should: they should really be sterilized before use. Sugar is used as a preservative in jams and jellies, and concentrated sugar is one of the few human foods for which food-poisoning germs do not care.

Smoking

Smoking consists partly of heating, partly of drying and partly of curing. The heating and drying are obvious results of the smok-

174

ing. The curing is more mysterious; it may come from strange pyroligneous acids in the smoke, possibly from traces of formaldehyde. Smoking adds a tang of flavour to the food and often tenderizes it, especially fish. It adds to its keeping qualities, but it does not sterilize it. Smoked sausages are often eaten without further cooking, but this is not a safe practice and fatal cases of botulism have been caused in this way. Smoked food, like any other cured food, is best cooked before being eaten.

Preservatives

Some chemicals may by law be added to some foods. Sulphur dioxide is one of the commonest. It may be added only to a specified list of foods and in prescribed concentrations. Sausages are in the list, as well as fruit pulp, dried fruit, grape juice, jams, mineral water, beer and cider. It has, of course, for centuries been used in wine-making, and it is most active as a preservative in acid solutions. It is very volatile and is driven off when any liquid containing it is boiled. It may therefore be used in high concentrations in fruit-pulp intended for jam making; when the jam is on the boil the sulphur dioxide can often be smelled and can even bring tears to the eyes.

Benzoic acid is another legally permitted preservative. It is used mainly in soft drinks, cordials, fruit juices, pickles and sauces and acts best in these acid conditions. It appears to be a harmless substance and is, in fact, present naturally in some fruits and vegetables in greater quantities than is allowed by law.

Sorbic acid added to flour, cheese and marzipan is active against yeasts and moulds. It seems to be harmless, for it is changed in the body into carbon dioxide and water. Propionic acid is another substance which attacks moulds. Moulds, of course, are killed when bread is baked, but other moulds may alight on the bread after baking and grow readily. This leads to a great deal of waste bread, but if propionic acid is added before baking, it keeps down mould growth afterwards. Propionic acid is present naturally in the body, and a small amount added to flour would appear to be harmless. People often object strongly to the addition of chemicals to food and, of course, care and thought must be exercised, but all food is composed of fats, carbohydrates and proteins, and these are, of course, all chemicals.

Radiation

When a patient is X-rayed, invisible rays penetrate his body and throw a shadow on a film placed behind or underneath his body. These rays consist of infinitesimally minute particles of electrically charged matter and they vibrate in a wide scatter of wave lengths. Gamma radiation is similar to X-radiation but the wave lengths are contained within a narrow band: it has similar powers of penetration. Both X-rays and gamma rays can have a damaging effect on the cells of the body, and it is for this reason that very strict precautions are taken in an X-ray department to protect workers and to limit the amount of radiation to which they are exposed. Just as the rays penetrate the body, so they can penetrate foodstuffs, and the principle behind radiation of food is to use the power of the rays to penetrate the food, while adjusting the dose of the rays so that germs are destroyed but the food itself not damaged in any way.

Gamma radiation has already been used on a large scale in medicine for the sterilization of syringes in this country, and also for the destruction of anthrax spores in hair imported to Australia. Its use in food is just getting beyond the experimental stage. It has certain advantages over other methods. It has very great powers of penetration and can be used to sterilize food after it has been canned or packeted. It can penetrate large joints or even carcasses, and bulked quantities of goods such as feeding stuffs. It produces scarcely any heat and can be used on frozen food such as poultry or frozen meat without raising the temperature more than a degree or two, if at all: in fact, radiation is possibly more effective at very low temperature and the dose can be reduced accordingly. It may be used to sterilize food completely, but sometimes a smaller dose is used to achieve only a reduction of germs. The term 'pasteuriza-tion' is used for this process just as it was in the canning of hams

(p. 170): but the difference with radiation pasteurization is that penetration is complete, whereas with heat pasteurization of solid food penetration cannot be guaranteed. The exact action of radiation is not fully understood, but at the dosage used for foodstuffs it probably acts mainly by energizing the atoms in molecules of water in the food and these, the hydrogen and hydroxide radicals, then become highly active chemically as reducing and oxidizing agents. Direct action on organic matter is probably minimal.

The possible uses of radiation are to destroy spoilage germs and so prolong the keeping life of food: and to destroy disease germs and so make it safe to eat. It could obviously be used to sterilize animal foodstuffs and this would attack salmonella infection at one of its main sources. It could also be used to sterilize carcass meat after slaughter and especially frozen imported meat. (It is probably effective against the virus of foot-and-mouth disease, and meat from countries where that disease is common could be rendered virus free before export—a great boon, indeed, if it comes to pass.) By destroying spoilage germs it would prolong the refrigeration or deep-freeze life of food, possibly indefinitely. Applied to fresh fish it would ensure its freshness throughout shop life. Meat, vegetables and other foods already in cans or packets could be sterilized without any alteration in texture or quality: this would remove the uncertainty which clings to pasteurized canned meats. It would destroy moulds on fruit and so make transport and distribution easier. It could possibly also be used for many agricultural purposes such as to delay the sprouting of seed potatoes or to eliminate insects or other pests from grain and other foods. It might also be used to destroy worms and similar parasites in food fed to farm stock.

These are all very satisfactory features of radiation applied to food. One of the main disadvantages is expense. Another might be organization, for it would hardly be possible to set up large numbers of widely scattered plants: but both these factors must be balanced against two advantages, the elimination of disease germs both in animals and man, and the saving of vast quantities of food which are lost by spoilage. More important than expense, however, is safety, and this is why radiation of food is still largely experimental. Toxic products might be induced by radiation or, far more serious, the food itself might become radioactive and its consumption be dangerous. All that can be said at the moment, as a result of experimental feeding of animals with irradiated food, is that neither of these hazards seem to occur with the doses used. Accidental overdosage might produce very grave danger. Another possible disadvantage of radiation might be its effect on the nutritive value of food, but all tests show that this is very slight, and not more than with other methods. We must, of course, not forget the germs themselves, for they do not readily give up the struggle for existence. They have already shown this by their ability to develop antibiotic resistance. There are just hints from experimental work that they may be able to develop radiation resistance. Man was caught unawares with antibiotic resistance: he must guard against this newer possibility.

Radiation of foodstuffs probably represents a break-through in food preservation, but for a long time yet we must depend on traditional methods. Even if radiation becomes the traditional method, the food hygienist will still have to remain vigilant, for irradiated food, like all other processed food, can still be contaminated after treatment.

Home Preservation

The housewife cannot compete with commercial preservers of food, and there have been many cases of botulism especially in Canada and America due to the inefficient home-canning of meat, fish and vegetables. *Clostridium botulinum* is not killed even after hours at 100° C. (212° F.). This is the temperature of boiling water, and therefore any method of canning or bottling meat, fish or vegetable which relies on boiling only is dangerous: the meat is certainly cooked, but, when it cools, the conditions inside the can are anaerobic (p. 39) and favour the growth of *Clostridium botulinum*. If these spores germinate they produce toxin inside the can or bottle, and if the food is eaten cold, even if the cook just tastes it before heating it, botulism is certain to follow. The toxin of botulism is destroyed by heat (p. 39) so that if the food is thoroughly heated, it might be safe to eat, but the risk is far too great.

The use of a pressure cooker may help the housewife who is determined to do her own home-canning. A good pressure cooker exerts a pressure of 0·7 kg./sq. cm. (10 lb./sq. in.) and this allows a temperature of 115·5° C. (240° F.) to be reached inside the can. This may be just enough to kill all the spores of *Clostridium botulinum*, but a temperature of 121° C. (250° F.) is safer and this is beyond the range of the household pressure cooker.

Acid fruits are much too acid for *Clostridium botulinum* so fruit bottling is completely safe, even without a pressure cooker. The same is also true for jams and jellies where the acidity and sugar concentration together defy any germs to grow. Sometimes a little condensation water forms on top of the jam beneath the cap, and, if air gets in, a few moulds may be able to grow there, but they are not dangerous. Pickles and chutneys are equally safe because of their acidity and sometimes also their sugar content.

The chief method of preserving open to the modern housewife is the deep-freeze, and the domestic deep-freeze does not differ from the commercial, except that the housewife depends on the deep-freeze to freeze and preserve the food, whereas the commercial operator usually freezes the food before storing it in the deep-freeze.

Freezing does not improve the food in any way. The housewife takes out exactly what she puts in. If the food she puts in is contaminated, it will be contaminated when she takes it out. The deep-freeze is convenient but not magic.

22

Housewife and Customer

The housewife shopping

'The customer is always right.' Always? Always right? In matters
of food hygiene she can be right *only* if she knows what is good
practice and *only* if she is prepared to insist on such practice where
she shops. This is not *always* easy. It requires a little courage to
object when the shopkeeper uses his hands instead of tongs on
slices of cooked meat she is buying, or opens paper bags by blow-
ing his breath into them, or handles raw meat and cooked meat
together, or wipes his hands on a wet rag. It requires courage, for
he is likely to protest that *his* hands and *his* shop are clean (but he
does not know the difference between clean and sterile). Even
worse, other shoppers, impatient of one's interference, but ignorant
of food hygiene, are likely to side with the shopkeeper and regard
as a crank, a fuss-pot and a nuisance the shopper who is merely
insisting on safe and wholesome food. But shopkeepers must satisfy
their customers, and must provide the standards their customers
demand. The occasional prosecution in court can deal with the
occasional case of gross bad hygiene, but every day in the shop the
informed customer can help to raise food hygiene standards. If she
does, she *is* always right.

The corner shop

In spite of chain stores and supermarkets the small corner shop
has not disappeared. Its great advantage is perhaps its convenience:
it is open at odd hours, there is less crush, and shopper and shopkeeper know one another. But the turnover is slower, and food

may therefore not be so fresh as in the big store. There are only one or two persons serving in the shop, so the same person handles all kinds of food, fresh, raw and cooked. There is only one set of scales, one slicing machine, one refrigerator, so that raw and cooked food are not kept separate. On the other hand, fewer varieties of food are stocked so there is perhaps less chance of cross-contamination. The personal element is an advantage and a disadvantage: the shopkeeper knows his customer's wants and can make sure she gets it when available, but she may find it a little difficult to protest when her friendly shopkeeper's practice falls below her standards of hygiene. On the other hand, an informed, intelligent small shopkeeper may find it easier to keep his eye on the details of good practice than does the manager of a multiple store. When things do go wrong in the small shop, fewer patients are involved for there are fewer customers, but small shops often get supplies from huge distributors and unsound food can in this way spread over wide areas (p. 142). So there are good and bad in the cosy corner shop. The keen housewife soon gets to know one from the other.

The greengrocer

Fresh fruit and vegetables are in Britain and in most countries very safe foods. (Odd methods of manuring can in some countries lead to dangerous conditions but the shopper in developed countries need not be concerned). One food-poisoning germ, *Clostridium welchii* (p. 36), can be introduced quite easily into greengrocers' shops on potatoes and other vegetables, but this germ will not multiply on vegetables, cooked or uncooked. If, however, it gets into meat stews it can flourish and cause food poisoning (p. 37). Now there is a tendency for greengrocers sometimes to sell foods other than vegetables and fruit and one occasionally sees cooked meats in such shops. The danger is perhaps slight, and one can, of course, avoid it completely by buying only vegetables and fruit in a greengrocer's shop. The real danger from *Clostridium welchii* on vegetables is in the kitchen rather than in a shop (p. 38).

The supermarket

Most of the food in the modern supermarket is tinned or pre-packed. Tinned food is very safe food (p. 62). Foods packed in cartons or packets and marked with the manufacturer's name are safe too, for large distributors cannot afford to be careless, and their production techniques are constantly under examination by expert food hygienists. When food is packed in Cellophane envelopes or more loosely wrapped, as is often the case with meat and meat products in supermarkets, safety depends on where and how the food was packed. In the larger chain stores this packing is done in large central kitchens or butcheries under expert supervision, but in smaller establishments facilities may be poorer and food may be contaminated during packing before the pack is sealed. If storage thereafter is faulty the packed meat may not be as safe as it looks. Packets of meat, and indeed unpacked meat, should not be sold from open counters in supermarkets, but only from refrigerated show cases.

In most large supermarkets different foods are served from different counters, meat from one, cheese from another and vegetables from a third and so on. This should always be the rule and there should never be movement of staff from one counter to another as otherwise germs may move with the staff. The turnover in the supermarket is vast so that food is usually very fresh, but the big turnover carries one disadvantage—if anything goes wrong it can go wrong on a large scale. (See 'A can of corned beef' p 197.)

Customers, of course, do most of their own serving from the shelves in the supermarket, and the girl who checks their purchases and handles their money does not also handle food. Perhaps we can look inside a typical shopping basket the housewife carries to the girl at the till.

The shopping basket

A typical basket might contain the following:
Tinned fruit—very safe indeed (p. 62).
Tinned meat—very safe (p. 62).

Frozen chicken—thawing and thorough cooking is important (p. 168).

Bacon—very safe, for cooking is always thorough.

Sausages—there may be germs in the centre so cooking *must* be thorough (p. 57).

Bread—very safe, too dry for germs (p. 146).

Cheese—made from pasteurized milk and so is safe (p. 104).

Packed meat—only safe if pre-packing is supervised
Should be date-stamped to check freshness.

Milk—safe if pasteurized.

Eggs—usually very safe (p. 102). Should be date-stamped for freshness.

Fruit—safe.

Pet food—safe if canned. Raw meat for pets may be contaminated.

Butter—safe: germs don't like fat (p. 107).

Lard or margarine—safe (p. 108).

Ice cream—safe because subject to legal standards (p. 114).

Yoghourt—safe if made from pasteurized milk; should be date-stamped for freshness.

Raw vegetables—safe, but should not come in contact with any unwrapped foods (p. 126).

The housewife, if she can carry it all, can take her load home fairly confident that her basket contains only wholesome food. Whether it remains wholesome till it reaches the table depends on how she behaves as housewife and cook.

The housewife at home

The trail of infection from farm and factory to the shop and the table can be a long and slow process (Chapters 5 to 8). At home the process can be greatly speeded up from the time the housewife brings the food into the house until she serves it on the table: food has to be handled, manipulated, heated, cooled, stored, re-heated and served and all the dangers of these processes on the large factory scale can be reproduced on a small scale, but much more quickly, in the home. Most food-poisoning outbreaks do, in fact, take place in the home. These outbreaks are known to the health authorities as 'incidents'; they do not hit the headlines or get on TV news, for only a few people are affected, but they cause a great deal of unnecessary illness and quite often admission to hospital and loss of school or working days.

Infection may be introduced to the home on the food the housewife has bought: salmonellae on meat, for example (p. 65), *Clostridium welchii* on vegetables (p. 65), or staphylococci on cream cakes. But these germs can also be added to the food in the housewife's kitchen. Germs passed in the faeces can get through toilet paper on to the hands, so hand-washing after the W.C. and before touching food is absolutely essential: germs passed in the faeces are not skin germs and can be removed by soap and water. Staphylococci *are* skin germs and are not so easily removed (p. 65), but most of them cannot cause food poisoning. The housewife should know that a sore on the fingers, on her face or anywhere on her body may contain dangerous staphylococci (she does not need to know their name), and that she must be more careful than usual when handling food. She ought to know that she can cause food poisoning in her family if she lets germs get into the food and that the main way of avoiding this is thorough cleanliness.

All the precautions about keeping raw and cooked food separate should be observed in the home: this does not require rigid separation in different rooms as in a factory, but just a little bit of commonsense in the kitchen: one should not, for example, prepare the raw joint for the oven and then, without washing, go on to make tomorrow's trifle or cream cakes: any salmonellae on the joint would be killed in the oven, but if any were transferred to the trifle or the cakes they could multiply exceedingly before the next day, or even in a few hours in a warm kitchen.

The greatest danger of food poisoning in the home does, in fact, lie in bad storage of food, especially cooked food. If she makes a trifle or a cream cake or, in fact, almost anything that is not to be eaten at once, that item should be stored in the refrigerator and kept there till just before required. Hot cooked food should be kept hot, *not* warm, till it is served and the interval should be as short as possible (p. 38). If the food must be kept till the next day, then it should be cooled *as quickly as possible* and put in the refrigerator. Remember, germs like warmth: most of them are killed by *heat*, and none of them multiply in the cold. Left-overs must be treated with great care: they often involve a good deal of handling—making them into rissoles etc.—and the very term 'left-overs' means they may be left for long times. But they must be left at a safe temperature, and that means inside the refrigerator, *not* in a warm pantry or kitchen.

Canned food is sterile, but only so long as the can is unopened. After the can is open the contents are exposed to the same hazards as any other food. Canned milk is a good convenience food, but it can become an excellent growth medium for germs once the can is open: it *must* be kept in the refrigerator. The same applies to bottled milk: if it is pasteurized it contains no disease or pathogenic germ (p. 104) so long as the bottle (or carton) is unopened: it does contain thermophilic (p. 171) or souring germs and these are only too ready to multiply if the pasteurized milk is allowed to become warm, and of course pathogenic germs can get in after opening, and they too will thrive in the warm milk. So the bottle should be in the fridge.

The use of the refrigerator requires some intelligence (p. 166). It is not a machine for killing germs, but only for stopping them multiplying. Germs in the food when it goes into the refrigerator are still there when it comes out, and they will start multiplying as soon as the outside temperature rises. A refrigerator will not function properly unless it is looked after: it needs cleaning and defrosting at regular intervals (p. 167). A deep freeze keeps food at a much lower temperature than a refrigerator: spoilage germs find it so much the harder to multiply, so food can be kept longer than in a refrigerator (p. 167). But even at the very low temperature of the deep freeze food-poisoning germs are not killed. When food is taken out and thawed any food-poisoning germs present will start to multiply; this is why food which has been thawed should not be re-frozen. Thawing must always be thorough before frozen food is cooked, because incomplete thawing may allow pockets of unfrozen food inside, and the heat of cooking may not penetrate these and germs deep in the food (for example, a chicken) would not be killed. To thaw a big chicken requires at least 12 hours (p. 168). To roast it thoroughly requires another $3\frac{1}{2}$ hours.

The housewife has responsibilities in the campaign for wholesome, safe food. She should tolerate nothing but the best standards in the shops she buys her food in, and be ready to object if she sees anything wrong. She can ask to see the manager if her complaints are disregarded: he is unlikely to treat them lightly if they are reasonable. She must remember, however, that her responsibilities do not cease when she leaves the shop. In her home she is her own manager and food hygienist.

23

Food and Travel

In the shop one can exercise control by not buying what does not please one. In the home and the kitchen the housewife is master, or mistress of all she surveys, if she knows how to survey it. But once leave home and one is in the hands of other people; literally in their hands if they are food-handling hands. This is the great age of travel; business or conference travel, travel for adventure or education, or, much more often, glossy brochure travel. From the food hygienist's point of view how safe is all this twentieth century coming and going?

Air travel

Meals during flights are part of the discipline of air travel. They are served not *to* order but *by* order. They can be unpredictable. A change of plane around meal times is hazardous: one can be faced with two main meals, one on each plane, within an hour or two, though it is equally possible to have no meal on either and be left to starve for half a day. We have even been wakened in the early hours to eat a dinner that should have been served the previous night but wasn't because the flight was delayed. On other delays we have been served a meal in the airport by courtesy of the airline, only to find, on finally boarding, that dinner was awaiting us as normal on the plane.

Airlines cannot afford to risk poisoning their passengers, and the standard of food hygiene is very high. But any pre-packed meal carries a risk. Time and temperature are important (p. 188). Germs on cold meats, raw fish or other sea food (p. 94) or on creams or sweets can be given just the conditions they like for multiplying. This is most likely in the poorer type of charter flight when meals for passengers on the return flight are already clipped to the backs of seats at the beginning of the outward flight, so that the food is held for several hours at cabin temperature. In general, a hot meal, if it is really hot, not tepid, is safe. The safety of a cold meal depends more on its handling before it is loaded on the plane than on anything that can be done to it on the plane. The standard of hygiene and the type of germ that might get into food varies in different parts of the world.

Episodes of food poisoning among passengers while still on the plane are rare—the incubation periods of most types of food poisoning are longer than the duration of most flights (p. 44). Staphylococcal food poisoning, because of its short incubation period (p. 44), could develop during longer flights: on one flight from Japan to London nearly all of 150 passengers were stricken and had to be landed at Copenhagen. How often passengers develop symptoms after the flight is not known. Probably not very often. Planes take people to odd places, and symptoms a day or two after landing may be due to something eaten after arrival, not in the air. But sometimes symptoms *can* be related to a meal during flight by bacteriological tests, for example, *Vibrio parahaemolyticus* food poisoning (p. 41).

Airlines are well aware of the risks, however small, of food poisoning from air meals, and some airlines have a rule that at least one pilot must have a meal quite different from that eaten by the passengers and the other members of the flight deck crew, so that if passengers and crew do go down with food poisoning, he remains unaffected. It is comforting to know that if the worst happens, there is always someone able to get the plane down safely.

Cruising

A week or two on the ocean wave provides a breezy break from life ashore. Unlike air travel, however, more than one meal is served during the voyage. Meals are, in fact, one of the main attractions of life on board, meals that thank goodness, says the housewife, someone else has had to prepare. But elaborate meals usually mean elaborate handling. The cold buffet is a popular feature but it has its dangers (p. 73). Obviously, enough food has to be carried to last from one port to another and usually facilities for storing this at the correct temperature are excellent on a cruise ship. Gone are the days when a carcase of beef was hung at the top of the mast to keep it in condition: the senior author once sailed on such a ship, but long before he knew anything about food hygiene.

Water has also to be stored, for ships are not connected to the mains, and sometimes water tanks have to be refilled at out of the way places where a pure water supply cannot be taken for granted. A few years ago typhoid fever broke out on an expensive cruise ship, probably caused by such a faulty supply of water. So there are food hazards aboard, and perhaps mild attacks of food poisoning, usually regarded as 'stomach upsets', are not uncommon. Shipping companies are well aware of their responsibilities regarding food hygiene, and sometimes they invite a bacteriologist and food hygiene specialist to sail on a cruise and investigate scientifically every item of food handling on board from the ship's store to the passenger's table.

Cruise ships call, of course, at interesting places and passengers often eat ashore. Conditions behind the scenes at some eating places can be more dramatic, at least to the food hygienist, than any of the advertised tourist sights, and symptoms that clients later develop on board should not be blamed on faulty ship hygiene.

Most cruise ships offer superlatively healthy holidays to their passengers, and it may seem churlish to dwell on the occasional unpleasant happening. But this is a book for serious food hygienists, not a glossy brochure for the travel trade.

Camping and caravanning

Camping and caravanning these days carry little hardship. From the food hygienist's point of view they have many advantages. Self-catering gives control over food supply and preparation: one knows what one is eating and who has prepared it. Food storage can cause problems and it is wise to shop daily for perishable food unless one has a refrigerator and it is big enough to cope. Milk can be difficult: it is much better to buy dried or evaporated milk than to rely on local fresh milk which is difficult to keep and may not be pasteurized. One soon gets used to the taste of dried milk in tea; if not, switch to lemon tea, which is more refreshing in hot climates.

Water from a high mountain torrent is usually safe to drink: there is no risk of contamination from sewage of animal or human origin. Low-lying springs and streams are dangerous for they can easily be contaminated (p. 86). If there is any doubt about the water, chloramine tablets can be added to it to sterilize it, but this is not reliable unless concentration of free chlorine can be checked, and campers don't often carry a laboratory with them. It is safer to boil such water, cool it, and then store it in bottles in the fridge or keep-cold bag. Big water carriers should be emptied and re-filled frequently: water is not a good medium for germs to grow in, but water becomes tepid inside a car or caravan and then some germs can flourish in it. The water supply in approved camps should have been approved by local authorities, but in remote areas such 'approval' may not be worth much. Ice, by the way, is not always a safe commodity to buy: the original water may have been safe enough, but ice-making involves manipulation, and this can sometimes be a little unorthodox. If all this fuss about water seems too complicated, one can stick to soft drinks, but these can be alarmingly expensive with a load of children aboard. It is much cheaper to make one's own lemon drinks with boiling water and fresh lemons, and drink this when cool: germs won't grow in such an acid medium.

Travellers' diarrhoea

Travellers' diarrhoea is one of the commonest epidemic diseases of the twentieth century. The diarrhoea usually afflicts the traveller a few days after arrival in some foreign country. It is not usually a serious condition, but it can ruin a short holiday, and be very inconvenient on a business or professional journey. Often it is put down to oily food, wine, the heat, sea-bathing or a combination of one or more of these, but there is little doubt that the condition is caused by germs in the food. Natives of the holiday centre do not suffer from it, probably because they have become immune to it over the years, but new arrivals have not encountered the germs before and so have no immunity. The germs are usually bowel germs, but the exact type of germ varies from place to place in different parts of the world. They get into food through faulty hygiene and they may get into water supplies if these are not protected by sound public health measures. Well-cooked food is safe, but uncooked food, especially salads, may be contaminated, as may creams, cold sweets, cold meats and especially left-overs. Various medicines are advertised to prevent this form of diarrhoea, but none can be guaranteed. The traveller can best protect himself by avoiding uncooked foods in the early days of his holiday and by not eating in doubtful restaurants or cafes. Germs do not grow in alcohol or oil: so in moderation neither commodity will do one any harm.

Is travel safe? It depends. It is as safe as the standard of food hygiene to which the traveller is exposed.

24

Food-borne Outbreaks

Examples draw when precept fails,
And sermons are less read than tales.

Prior

So far in this book we have done a good deal of preaching and the reader may well be tired of sermons. In this chapter we give some examples of outbreaks of food poisoning which emphasize points made in earlier chapters. Many of the outbreaks have been reported in full in scientific journals, and a list is given at the end so that students who feel inclined may read about them in more detail. These reports are really tales of detection.

A re-heated meal

One Saturday afternoon the midday meal served in an old people's home offered a choice of chicken or ham as the main course. Chicken was chosen by 130, ham by 72. Those who had chicken remained well, but 41 of those who ate ham suffered from severe gastro-enteritis and three of them died, two on the day after the meal, the third a few days later. The symptoms were diarrhoea and abdominal pain, but only four patients vomited. The illness began between 12 and 24 hours after the meal. The absence of vomiting is against staphylococcal food poisoning: the fairly long incubation period and the diarrhoea suggest either salmonella or *Clostridium welchii* poisoning (p. 44): the abdominal pain might suggest *Clostridium welchii* as the more likely cause, and this germ was grown from the faeces of the patients and from the intestines of the three who died.

The ham was boiled for 3 hours on Friday and allowed to cool in the kitchen for 1 hour. It was then skinned and bread-crumbed and put in the refrigerator at four o'clock in the afternoon. It was taken out on Saturday morning at 11.30 a.m., sliced or minced, and sent to the wards on trolleys to be served for lunch from midday till 1.30. None of the ham was kept after the meal so it could not be examined, but a similar ham was cooked in the same way, and a thermometer was then placed in it with its bulb at the centre of the ham. The temperature at the centre fell from 72·2° C. (162° F.) to 58·8° C. (138° F.) during the hour the ham lay in the warm kitchen: the outer layers of the ham would cool more quickly. It took 2 hours in the refrigerator to get the temperature at the centre down to under 20° C. (68° F.). During all this time the vegetative forms of *Clostridium welchii* could multiply quickly and produce toxin (p. 37).

The ham had been placed in the lower sections of the food trolleys to keep it cool until it was served. It was found, on testing, that in two of the trolleys, which were 20 years old, the insulation between the hot upper and cold lower sections was defective and the temperature in the lower section, 4·4° C. (40° F.) at the start of the test, rose to 18·3° C. (65° F.) in 1 hour and to 28·8° C. (84° F.) in 2 hours. At these latter temperatures *Clostridium welchii* might well begin to multiply again.

On the morning of the outbreak the trolleys were switched on at about 10.15 a.m. Most of the inmates who became ill had their lunch between one o'clock and 1.30 p.m., and most of them were served from the two defective trolleys. The cold ham would really have been tepid for some time before it was eaten. This outbreak illustrates the dangers of slow cooking and inadequate re-heating of food, and also the need to use good equipment. If the ham had been cooked on Saturday morning and eaten hot, there would have been no outbreak at all (Ref. 13, p. 221).

A salmonella tennis party

On a very warm June Saturday afternoon a tennis tournament was held in an English city. Cold barbecued chicken was served for tea in the afternoon and for supper at the dance in the evening. On Sunday morning one girl was taken ill at early mass, cases continued to occur all Sunday and by Monday about 40 of the tennis party were acutely ill, the main symptom being severe diarrhoea. Those who had chicken for supper seemed more ill than those who had it for tea: some who had chicken at both meals had the worst attacks of all. Towards the end of the week a second batch of patients became ill: they suffered a severe feverish illness which lasted for over a week, but they had very little diarrhoea. *Salmonella virchow* was grown from the faeces of all the patients: it was also grown from the blood-stream of the second group of patients.

The chicken had come from one cook shop in the town. On the Saturday morning deep-frozen chickens were taken out of the refrigerator, allowed to thaw out for an hour or two and then spit roasted for 1½ hours. They were then quartered, the portions were wrapped in grease-proof paper, packed in cardboard boxes and sent to the tennis pavilion in the early afternoon. They remained in the boxes in the warm pavilion till required for tea and later for supper.

Salmonella virchow was grown readily from many sites in the cook-shop, even from parts of the roasting spit: it was present in some other foods prepared in the same shop, and in the faeces of several people who worked there. It was grown from the carcasses of three birds after cooking. The frozen birds had been bought from a large poultry plant some miles away. *Salmonella virchow* was grown from several sites in this poultry plant. The chickens came from a group of rearing farms and *Salmonella virchow* was grown from dust, from chicken faeces and from one sample of food pellets. The chickens all came from a large hatchery, and *Salmonella virchow* was grown from dust in the hatchery and from the faeces of four workers there. The eggs came from a breeding farm, but the trail of infection did not go back so far and the germ was not found there, except in the faeces of one man who had also worked in one of the rearing units. The number of birds that might be infected between hatchery and poultry plant ran into several hundreds of thousands.

Chickens were sent from the poultry plant to shops over a wide area. One was sold in a country town to a farmer's wife. *Sal-*

monella virchow was later found in the overflow from the septic tank on the farm and from the soil in a field on which cattle were grazing. Nothing further happened there, probably because the danger was discovered quickly, but this part of the story does illustrate how far the trail of infection can go.

Why did the tennis party suffer so badly? The owner of the cook-shop did not know he was buying infected birds, but his premises were much too cramped. He had to use the same surface for thawing the raw birds and for cooling the cooked birds. The birds were not thawed properly: deep-frozen birds require about 12 hours to thaw (p. 168). The cooking time was too short even if the birds had been thawed: a chicken requires at least $2\frac{1}{2}$ hours for heat penetration (p. 70). The *Salmonella virchow* were still alive in the centre of the chicken after this inadequate treatment. In the warm pavilion that Saturday afternoon they could multiply at will. By tea-time there must have been hundreds of thousands on each leg of chicken and, by supper time, millions. Small wonder that those who had chicken for supper were iller than those who only had it for tea.

How the germ got into the farms is not known. It may have been in the feeding stuffs, though the feeding stuffs may have been contaminated from the air of the sheds. The workers were probably infected by their work on the farms, and were victims of, not the cause of the outbreak. The infection seemed to cause no active disease in the chicks or chickens: they thrived and appeared in excellent condition when they reached the poultry plant. This, of course, creates one obvious difficulty. If the infection does not harm the flocks, how can one expect the owners to take drastic steps to eradicate it? That is a veterinary, not primarily a food hygienists' problem.

Tests carried out on the deep-frozen chickens showed that if they were thoroughly thawed and thoroughly cooked, no *Salmonella virchow* survived. The chickens were then safe to eat so that attention to simple food hygiene principles solved that part of the problem. However the story of the salmonella on the chicken farms is not a happy one, nor easy to solve.

Chickens used to be a very safe food and outbreaks of food-poisoning in Britain were almost unheard of. This was probably because the birds were bought fresh and roasted at home in the oven. Changing food habits have altered this—we now have deep-frozen birds with the danger of incomplete thawing, and spit-roasting with the danger of poor heat penetration. We have also had a rapid growth of small barbecue shops and cafés where often the cramped conditions make good hygiene impossible. In another outbreak, very like the one above, *Salmonella montevideo* was grown from inside the roasted chickens, from the grills and spits, from the secateurs used for cutting the chickens and from the faeces of 8 of 11 staff. In yet another outbreak, this time in Canada, food-poisoning staphylococci were grown from legs of chicken in a warm display cabinet. There were 408 million staphylococci per gm. of chicken leg—quite a mouthful. One customer ate only a mouthful, but was in hospital, vomiting and collapsed, a few hours later (Refs. 15, 16, 19 and 20, p. 221).

Lamb's tongues in the canteen

Lambs are fairly innocent creatures both by nature and in the epidemiological sense, but there is almost no end to what man can achieve when he lays his hands on them, especially, as in the following incident, when his hands are not too clean.

Within 2 to 3 hours of a meal of braised lambs' tongues served in a factory canteen 50 workers were seized with severe vomiting, diarrhoea and abdominal pains: some were shocked and collapsed. The illness was due to staphylococcus food-poisoning, and when samples of the tongues were examined food-poisoning staphylococci were grown from them. How did they get on the lambs' tongues?

The tongues arrived at the canteen kitchen deep-frozen. They were thawed out and boiled for $2\frac{1}{2}$ hours. They were spread out on trays and, when cool enough to handle, were skinned by hand by 8 kitchen workers. The skinned tongues were then left for 2 to 3 hours till cool enough to go into the cold room where they were left overnight. At 8 o'clock next morning they were sliced and plated, and the plates were placed in the hot-plate container. The heat was turned on in the container at 11 o'clock and the braised lambs' tongues were served at midday. The containers had three shelves and the temperatures are interesting: on the bottom shelf it was 160° C. (320° F.), on the middle shelf 60° C. (140° F.) but on the top shelf only 42° C. (107·6° F.). Staphylococci could multiply happily on the top shelf (p. 35).

Swabs were taken from workers in the kitchen and staphylococci were grown from the hands or nose of eleven, but, and this is important, from only one man was a staphylococcus grown of the same type as caused the food poisoning. He had helped to skin the tongues. Two weeks later this staphylococcus was grown from the hands of four of the skinners and from the nose of a fifth. The hands of two of the workers remained positive for the staphyloccus for several weeks and it was grown easily from small cuts on their hands, even when the cuts were clean and healing. In fact, the germ seemed to find a cut an ideal place to multiply in and it was finally dislodged only after very determined treatments with antiseptics. These two men were, of course, not allowed to do any more skinning till clear of infection.

The kitchen itself was a poor place. The tables were wooden and the floor was rough: the staphylococcus was grown from the tables and from the floor dust. Crockery was washed in a dish-washing machine but had then to be stacked on a table uncovered, cutlery was washed in tepid water, and pots and pans had to be left on the floor as there was no room for them anywhere else. The cold room opened into the kitchen, so that dust and heat could blow in. In other words, a thoroughly unsatisfactory place for the handling of food. It is only too easy to see how the germs got on to the food and how they were given excellent facilities to multiply on it (Ref. 9, p. 220).

A can of corned beef

In May and June 1964 over 400 people in Aberdeen, Scotland caught typhoid fever. It was soon discovered that the earliest patients had eaten corned meat from a supermarket about a fortnight before they became ill. Later patients also had eaten cold meat, from the same shop, but not always corned meat. It became clear that meat contaminated with *Salmonella typhi* had been sold in the shop for about a fortnight during May. As soon as the infection was traced from the first cases to the shop, it was closed and disinfected. None of the original cans of corned beef was available for examination, but circumstantial evidence led fairly clearly to the source of infection.

The River Parana is a wide and fast river which flows past towns in South America and sewage from the towns flows into it. Below the towns, water is drawn off for many purposes, including the cooling of cans of meat in meat canning factories. There is a good deal of typhoid fever in South America, and typhoid bacilli could easily find their way in the sewage of the towns into the waters of the Parana River. Unless the cooling water were sterilized before being used, typhoid bacilli could enter a defective can during the cooling process in a canning factory.

One factory had a chlorinating plant but it had broken down and was out of use. The cooling water was used untreated straight from the river. If any can were to spring a leak during cooling (see p. 140), *Salmonella typhi* could enter that can and start to multiply. *Salmonella typhi* does not produce gas as it grows, so the can would not be blown: it is not a germ that causes putrefaction, so the meat could look sound and taste good. Cans of meat prepared in this factory in South America were sold to the supermarket in Aberdeen.

Possibly only one 6 lb. can was contaminated. When this was opened in the Aberdeen shop the meat was cut into two: one half was placed in the warm window, the other half was kept on a shelf behind the cold meat counter. When this second half was all sold, it was replaced by the first half and this was sliced and sold too. All the time, of course, the assistants were handling other pieces of cold cooked meats, cutting them with the same knife or slicing them on the same machine. Every evening all the unsold meats were collected and stored in a refrigerator: in the morning they were all brought out again and placed in the window or on the

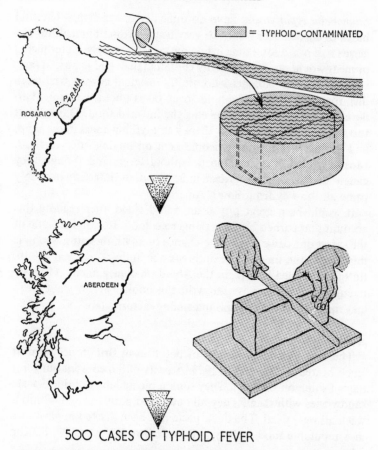

= TYPHOID-CONTAMINATED

500 CASES OF TYPHOID FEVER

FIG. 18. Cold water is used to cool hot tins in food factories. The water must be pure. Unchlorinated water in S. America probably led to typhoid fever in Scotland

counter. The hands of the assistants, the knives, the slicing machines, the shelves, the slabs and the counters were bound to become contaminated with *Salmonella typhi* from the first can of corned beef: and the infection was bound to spread to all the other cold meats. Once introduced into such an environment,

199

Salmonella typhi would have no difficulty in surviving. The first block of corned beef would be very heavily contaminated, for the germs had had a long time inside the can to multiply. Later pieces of meat would not be so heavily contaminated, and it was, in fact, noticed that the patients who ate the original corned beef were iller than the others. Typhoid fever takes about a fortnight to develop in a patient after he eats the infected food. During that fortnight no one could know there was anything amiss in the shop, and during that fortnight people kept on buying infected food. Most of them later developed typhoid fever, and though they caught the disease in Aberdeen in Scotland, the infection probably came all the way from South America.

It would be a great pity if anyone decided after reading this account that corned beef is a dangerous food. It is, in fact, one of the safest one can eat, and the chance of anything going wrong is minute. At the time of the outbreak the authors received a 6 lb. tin of the corned beef from the Aberdeen consignment. They ate it, enjoyed it, and survived to write this book. This does not mean they approve of carelessness in canning factories (Ref. 17, p. 221).

A fatal fishing party

The most famous outbreak of botulism in Britain occurred at Loch Maree in Scotland in 1923. A party of 8 men went out for a day's fishing on the loch. They took a picnic lunch of duck-paste sandwiches with them. They all developed paralysis and within a week all were dead. The duck-paste had been packed in glass jars in a reputable food factory and heated to 115° C. (239° F.) for 2 hours.

Clostridium botulinum is a fastidious germ, and slight changes in acidity, salt concentration or oxygen concentration may determine whether it lives or dies at a given temperature: something must have allowed them to survive in the glass jar. If the temperature had gone up to 121° C. (250° F.) the clostridia spores would have been destroyed. As it was, they survived and later germinated and produced toxin. Even so, the toxin is very easily destroyed by heat but, of course, the duck-paste was eaten cold. There have been only one or two isolated cases of botulism in Britain since the Loch Maree outbreak and these have been caused by home-preserved foods such as jugged hare, rabbit and pigeon pie and nut-meat brawn, always eaten cold. In Canada and America there have been many more cases of botulism from home-preserved foods: often string beans have been responsible, and sometimes only a taste before re-heating the food has proved fatal. Sometimes the food looks and smells a bit 'off', and on one occasion, when such food was thrown away, chickens that ate it died of botulism (Ref. 12, p. 221).

Left-overs for breakfast

One Saturday morning, within 3 hours of breakfast, over 40 soldiers were admitted to hospital in a garrison town on the Thames. Their symptoms were vomiting and diarrhoea. The short incubation period and the early vomiting suggested staphylococcal food poisoning, but *Shigella sonnei*, the germ of dysentery, was later grown from their faeces. Breakfast had consisted of fried fish rissoles and some were still available for inspection. *Shigella sonnei* was grown from them too. The rissoles had been prepared the night before by the camp cook, left all night in the kitchen and lightly fried in the morning, when they looked very appetizing. Unfortunately the cook was found to be a dysentery carrier. If the rissoles had been stored overnight in a refrigerator, or if the cook had not prepared them till just before frying them, perhaps there would have been no outbreak. As it was, the germs were given a whole warm night to multiply, and the light frying failed to sterilize the rissoles. Needless to say the chef was taken off cooking duties till his carrier state was cured.

The outbreak occurred nearly 30 years ago. Today food-borne outbreaks of Sonne dysentery are not so common: the disease is now more often spread by direct hand-to-hand contact.

Pink mince

The natural colour of dead meat is purplish red but this can be changed to bright pink if the meat is minced and mixed with nicotinic acid and ascorbic acid. In this way stale meat can be made to look fresh. Nicotinic acid is one of the B vitamins and ascorbic acid is vitamin C, both harmless in moderate doses. Nicotinic acid above a moderate dose makes the skin blood-vessels swell and this causes intense tingling, especially of the face, and often a wide-spread, pink blotchy rash. It is not a wholly unpleasant sensation, but it must have caused alarm when nearly 100 pupils and staff developed these symptoms within 15 minutes of eating hamburgers at school lunch. It was discovered later that the butcher had added a mixture of the two vitamins to the meat, but that the holes in the lid of the tin containing the powder were too large and let an excessive amount into the meat. This had the desired result on the mince, but the effect on the consumers was unexpected. It is an interesting story in that the addition of the chemicals was intentional, not accidental as in most cases of food poisoning. It also shows how substances, normally beneficial, can in certain circumstances produce alarming effects.

Shortly after this outbreak, the addition of nicotinic acid and certain other chemicals to meat was made illegal so that today, if mince is pink, it is probably fresh, not adulterated (Ref 4, p. 220).

A medical lunch

One would expect a buffet lunch for doctors to be a fairly well supervised and hygienic affair, but food-poisoning germs are not overawed even by a gathering of 150 prominent medical men. The doctors had cold chicken and ham for lunch, and within 3 hours 15 of them were in hospital suffering from vomiting, diarrhoea and prostration.

The chicken had been cooked the day before, split in half, and stored in a cool larder, not a refrigerator, overnight. In the morning they were placed on plates along with portions of canned ham and left to stand in the buffet room for about 3 hours. A staphylococcus was grown from samples of the chicken and ham, and also from the vomit and faeces of the stricken doctors. Both the chefs were examined: one had a nasal discharge and a staphylococcus was grown from it, but it proved to be a different phage

202

type (p. 34) and therefore could not have caused the outbreak. Where the food-poisoning staphylococcus came from is not known, but it was given ample opportunity to multiply once it got on the cold chicken and ham. Obviously not all the food was contaminated, for the attack rate among the doctors was quite low (Ref. 18, p. 221).

Safe and dangerous germs

Two outbreaks of staphylococcal food-poisoning occurred in London hospitals in 1961. Both were caused by cheese from New Zealand, so the germs had come a long way to cause trouble. The cheese was second grade. Such cheese was not meant to be eaten raw but is usually blended, heat-treated and processed. Somehow this lot reached the hospitals in the raw.

Cheese is made by adding a culture of bacilli to milk: these are known as the 'starter', and they acidify and curdle the milk. (This is not so terrible as it sounds: wine is also made by adding a starter of germs, yeast germs, to grape juice). Sometimes traces of antibiotics which have been used in the treatment of cows get through into the milk and this may be enough to prevent the starter from acting. If some resistant staphylococci are present in the milk, they readily take over: they acidify and curdle the milk but the cheese they make is poor stuff and has an off flavour. This is probably what happened in New Zealand, but it will not happen again, for all milk used for making cheese in New Zealand, as in Britain and most European countries, must now be pasteurized before the starter culture is added. Cream cheeses made in local farm-houses may still be dangerous: one small outbreak of dysentery was caused in France in this way, a most unusual occurrence. Any cheese bought in a shop in Britain today is wholesome and safe (Ref. 5, p. 220 and Ref. 23, p. 221).

St Paul and the ducklings

Ham, pressed beef, cold roast pork and a variety of other meats were all involved in a series of food-poisoning incidents during one week in Sussex. All the meats were bought in the same butcher's shop. *Salmonella saint-paul* was grown from the faeces of the patients.

The shop sold cold meats and raw meat and poultry. The cooked meats and the raw meat and poultry were sold from separate counters with separate staff. In the back shop, however, which measured only 10 ft. by 15 ft., the meat was cooked on a gas stove and then left to cool on a table only a few feet away from the bench on which ducks were eviscerated. It must have been quite warm in that small room with the gas stove on. Four members of the staff of 17 were found to be excreting *Salmonella saint-paul* in their faeces.

Thorough investigations were carried out. Farms which supplied pigs to the shop were visited and specimens taken from animals. The abattoirs which supplied the shop were also visited and specimens were taken of animal faeces and also of abdominal glands of animals after slaughter. Drain swabs of the abattoir were also examined and samples of animal feeding stuffs. Altogether several hundred specimens were examined in the laboratory and all proved negative. It looked as if the infection was not derived from the abattoirs or from the animals that passed through them.

When the poultry farm was investigated, *Salmonella saint-paul* was found in the faeces of some ducks and chickens. The chickens had been purchased as day-old chicks after the outbreak of the disease in the shops' customers, so could not have caused it. They were put into a brooder-house which also housed ducklings. This was the only building on the farm in which the *Salmonella saint-paul* was found, and ducklings had been reared in it and sold to the butcher's shop at the time of the outbreak. The ducklings had been fed on special crumb feeds which included meat from America. No other feeding stuff on the farm contained any American meat. When the feeding stuffs used on the farm before the outbreak were analysed, those which contained American meat were found to be more heavily contaminated with salmonellae than any other feeding stuff, although *Salmonella saint-paul* was not found in the samples examined.

When four of the staff of the butcher's shop were found to be excreting *Salmonella saint-paul* it would have been easy to conclude that they were the source of the outbreak and to search no further. However they had all eaten cooked meats from the shop at the time of the outbreak, and were victims rather than the causes of it. The finding of the salmonella in the ducklings on the farm showed that this was the true source of the infection. The ducklings, remember, were eviscerated on a bench only a few feet from the table with the slowly cooling meat on it. Salmonellae could easily have been transferred from the bench to the table.

There are at least three morals to this story. Raw meat and cooked meat should not be handled alongside each other. Cooked food should be cooled quickly, not left in a warm room. Investigations should always be thorough, and the obvious not taken too readily as the true cause of anything (Ref. 6, p. 220).

An innocent sore finger

Within a few hours of a school meal nearly one quarter of the pupils and staff were ill with sickness and vomiting: a few had diarrhoea. The meal consisted of mince and potatoes followed by a sponge containing a layer of artificial cream. Some members of the kitchen staff had cold ham instead of mince yet still became ill, so the sponge and the cream were obviously the cause of the outbreak. Staphylococci of phage type 42/E 53+ (p. 34) were grown from the cream. When the kitchen staff were examined the cook in charge was found to have a septic finger with a rather dirty dressing on it. Exactly the same type of staphylococcus was grown from the finger and the cook was, of course, suspended from duty. It seemed obvious that she was the cause of the outbreak, and certainly no one with a sore finger should be allowed to work in a kitchen. Further investigations showed, however, that the same staphylococcus was present in freshly opened tins of milk powder from the batch that had been used to make the cream in the kitchen. The cook's finger had therefore probably been infected by the milk powder and she was a victim rather than the cause of the outbreak. She should have known better than to have continued working with a septic finger, but the story does emphasize how thorough must be the detective work when trying to trace the trail of infection (Ref. 11, p. 221).

Bad angel cake

In the wide open spaces of Canada, workers on the highways cannot go home every night, but stay instead in road camps. These are usually well equipped, with good kitchen services. A small but severe outbreak of enteritis occurred in a group of labourers at one of these camps, and *Salmonella thompson* was grown from their faeces. The kitchen was clean and both the cooks were healthy and free from infection. All the foods served were investigated, and *Salmonella thompson* was grown from a cake-mix used to make angel cake. It was also present in samples of the cake-mix obtained from the shop that supplied the kitchen. The cake-mix contained egg powder and this was probably the source of the infection (p. 102). Now, *Salmonella thompson* is destroyed by baking temperatures (p. 30). The cooked cake must therefore have been contaminated after removal from the oven, either by the hands of the cooks or by dust from the uncooked cake-mix. The moral is obvious (Ref. 22, p. 221).

A pie that closed a school

Pork pies contain a well balanced supply of carbohydrates, protein and fat, and as such provide plenty of energy for hungry schoolchildren. They should not also contain germs. Unfortunately one batch of pork pies did, and 80 schoolchildren, five teachers and three domestic workers all got salmonella food poisoning and the school had to be closed for several days. A portion of pie was found in a dustbin and *Salmonella typhimurium type 2a* was grown from it. The same germ was grown from the faeces of the patients.

When the food factory was investigated the same germ was grown from the drain of the pie department, from the w.c. pan for female staff and from the faeces of three women who made the pies. One of the three added gelatin to the pies after cooking (p. 59), and it was probably here that the dangerous contamination

206

took place, for any salmonella added to the pies by the other two women would probably have been killed in the oven. The factory had its own slaughterhouse and raw meat department, and the same *Salmonella typhimurium* was grown from a drain swab there. The germ probably entered a live pig, got on to the raw pork, and infected some of the workers, one of whom contaminated the gelatin that was added to the cooked pies. Its presence in drains shows how a germ can get around once it gets into an environment that suits it (Ref. 8, p. 220).

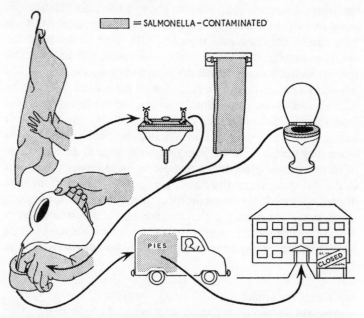

= SALMONELLA–CONTAMINATED

FIG. 19. Germs got in when the gelatin was poured into these pies, and food poisoning closed a school

The glazed liver

The contamination of the pies after they were cooked and sterile recalls another much bigger outbreak caused by liver sausage loaves in a large factory. The sausage was sold to shops as far apart as Newcastle and London and outbreaks of food poisoning were reported by 44 different Medical Officers of Health. The sausage loaves were sterile after cooking: indeed the centre of some of the sausage examined after the outbreak was still sterile. The glaze applied over the sausage loaves was very heavily contaminated with staphylococci type III, 6/47.

This glaze was a compound of water, gelatin, pigs' feet jelly, lard and beef dripping. It took several hours to prepare and its temperature was well below 60° C. for most of the time. Some of the dripping was crumbled into the glaze by hand, and 11 different people handled the sausage during the glazing process with their bare hands. Staphylococci type III, 6/47, were grown from the hands or nose of 6 of these workers: one man also had a septic sore on his forehead and the same germ was present in the pus. His job was to render down the lard, one of the hottest jobs, but he used a roller towel in the mens' lavatories and the germ was grown from this too. The other men could have got the germ on to their hands from the towel, and they handled the glaze and the loaves when they were quite cool. Samples of the glaze at an early stage of its production grew only a few germs, but samples taken later in the day grew many thousands per gramme. Many rules were drawn up to prevent a recurrence: these included a no-touch technique when handling the sausage loaves and the glaze, a different recipe for the glaze requiring a much higher temperature in its preparation, and the abolition of roller towels (Ref. 2, p. 220).

A craving for coconut

Pregnant women often hanker after unusual articles of diet. One woman in Liverpool had always liked raw desiccated coconut, and when she became pregnant in 1960, her liking became a craving and she ate large quantities for several months. In the maternity hospital she developed diarrhoea and vomiting, and an unusual type of *Salmonella paratyphi B* was grown from her faeces. She infected her own infant and 4 others. Another woman became ill with gastro-enteritis due to the same germ, and 7 other adults in the ward, 6 of them members of the staff, became carriers of the germ, though they did not become ill. Altogether 14 people were infected with the coconut germ.

It had been known for some time that salmonellae, including this unusual type, were being imported in coconut, mainly from Ceylon. Investigations in that country showed that the collection, chopping and grinding of the coconut husk were carried out under conditions that could easily lead to gross contamination of the dried or desiccated coconut. The salmonella might not grow well on such dry material but it would survive, and when dusted on to a moist cake some thousands of miles away it would begin to grow again and could then cause outbreaks of disease. The hygiene of the exporting countries has been greatly improved, and coconut in Britain is now heat-treated before being distributed. There is nothing quite like the flavour of desiccated coconut. It is now quite safe to eat it in Britain (Ref. 3, p. 220).

Faggots or sausages?

Between 7 and 24 hours after Sunday morning breakfast of sausages and faggots four families in Shropshire were stricken with abdominal pain and diarrhoea. (Faggots are made from liver and offal, wrapped in pig's caul and boiled, a bit like haggis, but more mysterious.) All the patients had eaten sausage, some had faggots as well: but none who ate only faggots was upset. Two patients ate their sausages raw: their illness was much more severe and it came on quicker.

Salmonella dublin was grown from the faeces of all the patients, and also from lightly cooked sausages and a piece of faggot collected from one of the houses. The sausages and the piece of faggot were packed in the same container, and probably germs spread from the sausages to the faggot on the way to the laboratory, for the faggots had been boiled in the shop for 6 hours, and salmonella would not survive such a treatment. Moreover, the faggots caused no illness.

More cases occurred soon after; these patients had also eaten sausages, but not from the same shop. One abattoir supplied both shops. Unfortunately we cannot tie the story up by saying that *Salmonella dublin* was grown from the abattoir, but conditions were certainly bad enough to allow salmonellae to spread: a cloth used for wiping carcasses was also used for wiping the slaughterer's boots. A few days before the outbreak, five cattle had been slaughtered, and a side from each was sent to both the sausage manufacturers. All of the five cattle were, in retrospect, regarded as 'of low grade'. One or more of them might have been infected with *Salmonella dublin* which is a common disease germ of cattle.

Although the bacteriologists did not find the salmonella in the abattoir, they did prove that it could survive light frying. They dipped thermometers in a culture of *Salmonella dublin* and inserted them lengthwise into sausages. They then fried the sausages for varying periods and at various temperatures in the laboratory. They concluded that *Salmonella dublin* could survive gentle frying for 15 minutes, though brisker frying killed the salmonella quickly. The moral is obvious: faggots are safer than sausages, but if you prefer sausages, as we do, fry them thoroughly and brown them on all sides. Don't, whatever you do, eat them raw.

Since 1968, by the way, the use of a cloth for wiping carcasses has been made illegal in Britain, whether or not the cloth is also used for wiping the slaughterer's boots. Instead, carcasses are now sprayed with clean water, and dirty rags have been banished from our abbattoirs (Ref. 10, p. 220).

Bitter sweet

Pavlova cakes would seem very suitable sweets to eat at a ball, but only if no mistakes are made in the baking. At one dance in New Zealand 40 of 150 guests were seized with severe vomiting and diarrhoea $1\frac{1}{2}$–2 hours after refreshments, an occurrence causing some inconvenience. After complicated investigations it was found that at the bakery 10-lb. bags of potassium bromate were weighed and packed on a bench beside the sugar bin, and the same scoop was used for sugar and potassium bromate. This chemical is used as a flour improver and is harmless in the correct amount. Unfortunately it looks very like sugar, and someone must

210

have left some in the scoop, and someone else must then have put this in the cakes instead of sugar, for potassium bromate was later found when cake crumbs were analysed. The symptoms and the short incubation period had at first suggested staphylococcal food poisoning (p. 45), but all bacteriological tests were negative. Other cases occurred in the neighbourhood, and tea, coffee and infant food was suspected. The common factor seemed to be 'sugar', and careful detective work led to the scoop on the bakery bench. The patients fortunately recovered quickly, but the outbreak must have ruined the ball.

Mistakes such as the above are not common, but they should never occur at all if foodstuffs and chemicals are properly and clearly labelled. Two very serious outbreaks of food poisoning occurred in Israel due to the eating of sausages which contained barium carbonate instead of potato starch. The two substances *looked* alike, but were very different in every other way. The symptoms included vomiting and diarrhoea, but also severe weakness and paralysis. Two patients required artificial respiration in a breathing machine, and one patient died (Ref. 1, p. 220 and Ref. 14, p. 221).

Trouble over a trifle

One afternoon in a mental hospital, 6 out of 38 patients developed acute vomiting and diarrhoea between a $\frac{1}{4}$ and $\frac{1}{2}$ hour after tea. They blamed the tea, but this consisted only of bread and butter, treacle and tea. Moreover, two of the patients had felt ill earlier in the afternoon and tea just seemed to trigger off the illness. For their midday meal they had beef croquettes and trifle with custard. The beef croquettes were freshly prepared and cooked just before the meal. The trifle and the custard had both been made the day before, and left to stand at room temperature all night.

Staphylococcus Type 31/44 was grown from the faeces of the patients. The trifle and custard had been greatly enjoyed at lunch time and none was left for examination. Swabs were taken from

211

noses of the patients, from the nurse in charge of the ward, from persons who served the trifle and from the chef who made it the day before. No staphylococcus of type 31/44 were grown except from the nose of the chef, and he was shown to be a heavy nasal carrier of the germ. He prepared the trifle by hand and could easily have added staphylococci to it from his nose. Being left overnight in a warm room they would have plenty of time to multiply. Somehow, the chef must have infected only part of the trifle, for only 6 of the patients who ate it became ill. Perhaps he used his handkerchief or picked his nose after he had made most of the trifle and so just infected the last portion (Ref. 7, p. 220).

An unfortunate house party

In the summer of 1936 over 500 people fell ill with typhoid fever in a south coast town, and another 200 who had spent a holiday there became ill when they returned home. It was obviously 'something they had eaten', and it was soon clear that milk from one dairy was the common factor. The owner of the dairy had built up a reputation for the rapid delivery of fresh farm milk, but he immediately accepted pasteurization as soon as he was informed that his fresh milk had caused the outbreak. No new cases occurred from drinking the pasteurized milk.

The dealer received about 1,600 gallons of milk daily; 12 roundsmen delivered it and cases occurred in every man's milk round. Clearly the milk at the dairy was infected, but tests on all the workers there were negative. The germ must already have been in the milk when it reached the dairy, and if it was present in one batch of milk it could easily spread through the rest, for all the milk was bulked in the dairy before dispatch to customers. The milk came from 37 different farms. All these were visited and 192 persons who had handled milk were examined. All the investigations were negative except at one farm where the farmer's wife was found to be suffering from typhoid fever. Shortly afterwards, her son also became ill. When the farmer's wife first became ill there were already over 20 cases of typhoid fever in the town. Clearly, she was a victim of the epidemic, not the cause of it.

212

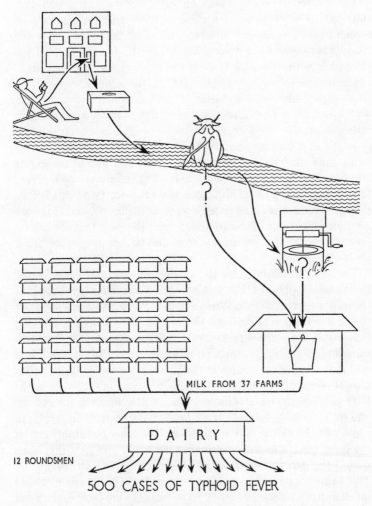

MILK FROM 37 FARMS

12 ROUNDSMEN

DAIRY

500 CASES OF TYPHOID FEVER

FIG. 20. Tracing an epidemic is like solving a crime. In this case there were 37 clues, but only one led to the 'scene of the crime', a typhoid carrier in a country house

213

The farmer drew his supply of water from a well which also supplied 10 other houses. In none of those was there a case of typhoid fever. It seemed unlikely therefore that the well water could have caused the epidemic, though the farmer washed his milk pails with it and his standard of hygiene was not very high. A stream ran through a meadow 100 yd. from the house, and the cows grazed alongside and often waded into the water. A short way upstream a pipe discharged the effluent from a septic tank into the stream, and from this effluent *Salmonella typhi* was grown, and it was the same type as had caused the epidemic. The septic tank drained a large country house, and one of the guests was found to be a typhoid carrier. He had suffered from a severe fever which nearly killed him many years before. Two years before the epidemic he had again been a guest at the house, and that year a young girl in one of the 10 houses near the well died of typhoid fever. She often ate watercress from the stream and drank from the well.

The connection between the carrier and the 500 cases in the town seemed obvious, but just how the *Salmonella typhi* got into the milk was not so clear. When a fluorescent substance was added to the stream it was detected in the well 100 yd. away, showing that water from the stream could reach the well. Whether *Salmonella typhi* could get through was more doubtful. If it did, it is odd that none of the people in the 10 houses who drank the water caught typhoid fever, though the dose of germs in the water might have been quite small. Milk is a much better medium for growth and the dose of *Salmonella typhi* would have been much greater in those who drank the milk in the town. The other possibility is that the cows were infected by drinking the water and that they then passed the germ in their faeces and urine or even in their milk. This sounds a convincing theory, but cows do not become readily infected with *Salmonella typhi*. Experiments were later carried out to try to infect cows with *Salmonella typhi* derived from the carrier who caused the outbreak. Even with massive doses by mouth, or by injecting the germ into the milk ducts, it proved almost impossible to infect the cows. *Salmonella typhi* seems to cause disease in man only. The other possibility was that when the stream was swollen with rain the cows wading in it might soil their udders with *Salmonella typhi*, which then got into the milk. The evidence from the epidemic, however, suggested that the milk had been contaminated for several weeks and it was very unlikely that the outside of the udders could have been soiled all that time. The farmer apparently did not use water directly from the stream. As often happens in any kind of detective work it was impossible, after the event, to close every link in the chain of circumstantial evidence. Between the moment of infection and the first sign of illness in typhoid fever 12 days pass, and in that time one vital circumstance can easily change. The chain was there, but one link was missing (Ref. 21, p. 221).

Streptococci in the camp

A holiday camp provides carefree holidays for the holiday-maker, but behind the scenes the organization is certainly not free from care. When we visited one camp and saw trolleys of meat pies being wheeled into the dining hall, we were told that 90,000 identical pies would at that moment be going into dining halls in other camps throughout the country. This is catering on the massive scale. It is also big business, and big business cannot afford even minor food hazards. So food hygiene in such organizations must be of the highest standards. A minor slip can lead to a major disaster.

Nine thousand people were holidaying in a holiday camp in Britain. Most of them arrived in time for lunch one Saturday. By Tuesday over 100 were ill with tonsillitis, by Wednesday 350 were ill and by Thursday the total number was over 550. Such an outbreak of tonsillitis is most unusual. Normally the germ of tonsillitis spreads in droplets from the throat of one person to the throat of another and it would take weeks to spread to so many people. This dramatic outbreak could be spread in one way only, by the germ getting to some food or drink. How to trace it?

Six thousand of the campers did their own cooking and catering in their chalets; 3,000 fed in the dining hall. It became clear on questioning that only those who fed in the dining hall got tonsillitis. The germ grown from their throats was a streptococcus, a common tonsillitis germ but an uncommon cause of food poisoning. The menu for every meal served from Saturday to Monday was scrutinized and patients were questioned *discreetly* about what they had eaten. The search was for an article of food common to all the patients, one probably served cold or uncooked, and it soon became clear that artificial cream served with tinned fruit was the likely item. All those who became ill on Tuesday or Wednesday had eaten cream, and no-one who had not eaten cream became ill on either of those two days. Several people ate a lot of cream and they had severe attacks. One father ate his own cream and the portions of his three children who did not like cream; he was one of the illest patients. Of those who did not become ill till Thursday some had eaten very little cream and so presumably got only a small dose of germs; a few had not eaten any cream at all, but all of them were members of the same families and slept in the same chalets as some who became ill on Tuesday or Wednesday. So there were two ways of getting the same tonsillitis: most patients got it by swallowing germs in the cream, and a few got it by inhaling germs breathed out by relatives or friends who already had the tonsillitis from eating cream.

The artificial cream came to the camp in one-gallon plastic containers. One gallon provided portions for 200 people, but three containers were always emptied into one pail some time before being served in the dining hall. One pail would then contain enough portions for 600 people. If one container was infected with streptococci before arrival at camp, the germs would get a chance to multiply in the pail in the kitchen and one pail would then contain enough streptococci to infect 600 patients. Actually there were over 550 cases of tonsillitis, and as some of the diners did not take any cream, the figures seemed to fit the facts very neatly. Several samples of cream were examined but no germs were found, but, of course, as so often happens in food-poisoning outbreaks the original containers had been thrown away and none of the cream served on Sunday evening was available for examination on Tuesday or Wednesday. The evidence, as they say in court, was circumstantial, but the circumstances were fairly convincing.

In these days of pasteurized milk tonsillitis has become a rare form of food poisoning, although in the old pre-pasteurization days tonsillitis, scarlet fever and even diphtheria could be spread by milk. Food poisoning to most people means diarrhoea and vomiting, not sore throats, and in this outbreak none of the patients suspected they were victims of food poisoning. Radio, television and press were also silent: one can imagine the coverage that 550 cases of food poisoning in a holiday camp would have attracted. But to what purpose, except sensation? As it was, though questioning of patients was discreet, everyone behind the scenes, from top management to kitchen staff was deeply concerned, officers of the Public Health Department were called to the camp at the first sign of the outbreak, and every aspect of the supply, preparation and distribution of food was investigated in minute detail. No fault in the camp catering arrangements was found, but somewhere, probably in the artificial cream factory, streptococci, possibly from some carrier's throat, got into one plastic container, and from then on, warmth and moisture allowed them to flourish.

25

Past, Present and Future

Things past belongs to memory alone;
Things future are the property of hope.

Home

We began with the cave-man, with nature in the raw. Whether salmonellae, staphylococci and clostridia troubled him much we do not know. If they were present in his cave they must have had to fight as hard as he did to survive, for his hand-to-mouth existence gave them little chance to settle down and multiply in his food or on his kitchen equipment. With civilization came sophistication, and food-poisoning germs have had a good time of it. They could not themselves have arranged things so well as man in his ignorance has done for them. They could never have invented the Food Handler, yet nothing has been of such assistance to them as that kindly manipulator of their environment. They have had a rough time of it in some areas, and many have come to grief in a sterilization plant: but, on the whole, life has gone smoothly for them and the species have never been in any danger of extermination. What of the future?

Food habits change, often very quickly. Dining out has not always been the popular pleasure it is today, and spit-rotisseries and barbecues have shot up almost quicker than proverbial mushrooms. The deep-freeze is in every shop and many houses, and there are supermarkets on every High Street. These are all profound changes, and they all present a challenge. They give great opportunities to control infection at its source, but, if things go wrong, we get disasters, not minor outbreaks. The food hygienist has heavier not lighter responsibilities.

How far can we see ahead? Many blocks of flats have restaurants

218

for the residents. If blocks of flats, why not blocks of houses, or streets? Is there not something absurd in the situation where thousands of small ovens are all cooking at the same time, when one or two giant ovens could do the job at least as well? After all, no housewife now bakes her own bread. Why should she roast her own joint? Male hands may be held up in horror at the prospect of no home cooking, but the modern housewife is getting tired of drudgery.

One cannot foresee the future, however hard one looks ahead. One can only be sure there will still be a challenge. The spit-rotisserie and the deep-freeze have increased, not decreased the problems of food poisoning from poultry. Radiation may abolish it, or, as we have hinted, it may bring new problems. The man in the moon may soon replace the man in the street. He will still have to eat. Food hygienists will need all their skill to guarantee the purity of The Food We Eat.

References

1. Agen, S. Rosenbluth, S. and Eisenberg, A. (1967). 'Food poisoning due to barium carbonate in sausage.' *Israel J. med. Sci.* 3, 565.

2. Allison, V. D., Hobbs, Betty C. and Martin, P. H. (1949). 'A widespread outbreak of staphylococcal food poisoning.' *Month. Bull. Minist. Hlth.* 8, 38.

3. Anderson, E. S. (1960). 'The occurrence of *Salmonella para-typhi* B in desiccated coconut from Ceylon.' *Month. Bull. Minist. Hlth.* 19, 172.

4. Cust, G. (1965). 'An outbreak of unusual food poisoning.' *Med. Officer.* 113, 124.

5. Epsom, J. E. (1966). 'Staphylococcal food poisoning due to cheese.' *Med. Officer.* 112, 105.

6. Galbraith, N. S., Mawson, K. N., Maton, G. E. and Stone, D. M. (1962). 'An outbreak of human salmonellosis due to *Salmonella saint-paul* associated with infection in poultry.' *Month. Bull. Minist. Hlth.* 21, 209.

7. Gillespie, E. H. (1947). 'Staphylococcal food poisoning. The possible source traced by means of bacteriophage typing.' *Month. Bull. Minist. Hlth.* 6, 8.

8. Harding, K. M. (1966). 'An outbreak of food poisoning following the consumption of infected pork pie.' *Med. Officer.* 115, 159.

9. Hobbs, Betty C. and Thomas, Mair E. M. (1968). 'Staphylococcal food-poisoning from infected lambs' tongues.' *Month. Bull. Minist. Hlth.* 7, 261.

10. Jones, A. C. and Symons, A. D. (1948). 'An outbreak of food poisoning due to *Salmonella dublin* conveyed by sausages and sausage meat.' *Month. Bull. Minist. Hlth.* 7, 202.

11. Leff, S. (1957). In *Recent Outbreaks of Infectious Diseases.* Lewis: London.

12. Leighton, G. R. (1923). *Report of the Circumstances attending the Deaths of Eight Persons at Loch Maree, Ross-shire. Official Report to the Scottish Board of Health.* Edinburgh: H.M.S.O.

13. Parry, W. H. (1963). 'Outbreak of *Clostridium welchii* food poisoning.' *Brit. med. J.* 2, 1616.

14. Paul, A. H. (1966). 'Chemical food poisoning by potassium bromate. Report of an outbreak.' *New Zealand med. J.* 65, 33.

15. Pennington, J. J., Brooksbank, N. H., Poole, Pauline M. and Seymour, F. (1968). '*Salmonella virchow* in a chicken-packing station and associated rearing units.' *Br. med. J.* 4, 804.

16. Pivnick, H., Barr, T. R. B., Erdman, I. E. and Pataki, J. I. (1968). 'Staphylococcus food-poisoning from barbecued chicken.' *Can. J. publ. Hlth.* 59, 30.

17. Report (1964). *The Aberdeen Typhoid Outbreak 1964.* Edinburgh: H.M.S.O.

18. Report (1968). 'Food poisoning at B.M.A. House.' *Communicable Disease Report* 68/27.

19. Report (1968). '*Salmonella montevideo* food poisoning at Bath.' *Communicable Disease Report 68/26.*

20. Semple, A. B., Turner, G. C. and Lowry, D. M. O. (1968). 'Outbreak of food poisoning caused by *Salmonella virchow* in a spit-roasted chicken.' *Brit. med. J.* 4, 801.

21. Shaw, W. V. (1937). 'Report on an outbreak of enteric fever in the County Borough of Bournemouth and in the boroughs of Poole and Christchurch.' *Report Publ. Hlth. Med. Subj.* No. 81. H.M.S.O.: London.

22. Skoll, S. L. and Dillenberg, H. O. (1963). 'Salmonella thompson in cake-mix.' *Can. J. publ. Hlth.* 54, 325.

23. Szturm-Rubinstein, S., Courtieu, A. L. and Maka, G. (1964). 'Un fromage contaminé par *Shigella sonnei* cause d'intoxication alimentaire.' *Bull. Acad. nat. Méd.* 148, 480.

Carol A Evans.

Index

222

230